ROMANCE
OF A
HAREM

Translated by
CLARENCE FORESTIER-WALKER

PRIVATELY PRINTED FOR THE
HOGARTH PRESS
NEW YORK

PREFACE TO SECOND EDITION

IN answer to innumerable letters from known and unknown correspondents, as to how much of " The Romance of a Harem " is true ; it has been thought advisable by the publishers that I should acknowledge that it is an absolutely true story.

The authoress's father (when the writer was a small child) was sent by the French Government on a mission to the Sultan, who received him and his family on terms of the greatest intimacy, and who had a profound respect for the distinguished French gentleman.

It was with her father and mother that the authoress learnt the Turkish language, and visited during her youth, before marriage, all the leading Turkish families, and thus gained what is so rare among Europeans, an intimate knowledge of the little-known private life of great harems.

This true story, as given to the public, was known and approved of by the children of Prince Halim, who plays so large a part in the romance.

It was on reading this story, and its successor, " La Courtisane de la Montagne,"*in the original, that His Majesty, the present Sultan, issued an irade, forbidding the employment of European governesses in Turkish harems.

CLARENCE FORESTIER-WALKER.

* English Edition entitled " The Woman of the Hill."

ROMANCE OF A HAREM

—

CHAPTER I

FOR many a long year I lived in a harem, and of that time I have the sweetest remembrances. Comparisons that I have been able to make since the chances of fortune led me to share the life of European women, only strengthen the tender melancholy of those souvenirs.

The natural sentiments of women—affection, devotion, and the decency of life—become strongly developed in the warm and favourable atmosphere of a harem. What a peaceful charm! what a profound calm there is in those vast rooms half-filled with shadow!

Sitting on her cushions, with her bare feet crossed beneath her, she sees through the carved grating the boats that glide past on the Bosphorus. She slowly smokes a scented cigarette, and sips languidly her coffee from a tiny cup.

On her white brow, which no care wrinkles, the beautiful Circassian arranges her sequins, and sings to herself in a minor key; she thinks only how to preserve her beauty, and rests after the complicated *soins* of the bath, and slowly tastes the joy of pleasing; she plays with the children, and to amuse herself has a thousand puerile incidents which fill the hours. I have known all that; but if I grew up in the peace of the harem, loved and respected, I also have seen only too closely the dramas of oriental politics and peaceful existence of the sultanas and odalisques upset by the so-called progress of European morals. The death of the last of the real great Mussulmen—the man to whom I

owed the most profound respect, has de-
livered me from the promise I gave that
I would never write for publication during
his life-time, and I shall be glad if I can
show how false are many of the ideas of
life in a harem.

Nearly always the repose and dignity of
the harem is broken by the English or
French governess whom it is the fashion
to employ to initiate the young Turkish
girls into the beauties of European education. Happily the influence of the *Miss*
or *Madame* or *Mademoiselle* is of an
ephemeral duration. These governesses
shock the oriental women who have
regard for their proper dignity, and seldom succeed in inoculating them with
their ideas. They come from Paris, or
more often from Marseilles. Their doubtful
morality has generally left them little chance
of honest employment in their own country.
I remember one of them whose influence

was fatal to a charming young woman. This *Mademoiselle* had originally been a singer in a *café-concert*, and being furnished with a letter from a celebrated Armenian archbishop, easily installed herself in the house of this young married lady, inducing her to commit a thousand foolish actions, which ultimately forced the husband, who was aide-de-camp to His Majesty, to get a divorce.

Amongst all these governesses in search of adventures, I must mention one exception in favour of Miss Albert, whom I knew during my childhood, and who brought up the daughters of the Egyptian Prince M——— F———. She had been recommended to His Highness by a member of the English royal family. She left behind her a reputation for European honesty, and was much loved and respected. Therefore let us put in upon record that there was once a respectable European governess in Turkey —and she was English. Nevertheless, this education only brought disorder in the ideas of the young Turkish women. The Princesses—the pupils of Miss Albert—were far from happy. One of them, the widow of the famous K— Pacha, celebrated in Paris under the Second Empire, gravely compromised herself with an immensely rich Jew; she was obliged to leave Constantinople for Cairo, where, since the occupation, she has laden the English with her favours, though she is over fifty years of age.

For the matter of that, Europeans seem very much to appreciate the beauties of other days.

One—a rich and amiable diplomat of a little country in the north—recently eloped with a much compromised and somewhat matured beauty, which caused the Khedive to say: "Thank Heaven! when our foolish women become old, some European is always ready to relieve us of them."

All this is very unfortunate, but difficult

to avoid, and the rich harems will for a long time be given up to this false education, the Turks being in an impossible position for obtaining true knowledge about the governesses that are sent to them.

It is a mistake to believe in the possibility of any real education being given to the oriental women—a mistake spread by the few European women who are occasionally admitted for an hour or two into the harems. They have never really understood the true character of the family, or of Turkish households. *Mademoiselle* introduced doubtful novels or undertook the delivery of *billets doux* to the attachés at the embassies, which without her assistance were entirely deprived of oriental distraction.

The wise man understands that there is little real love outside the harem, and is afraid of the unknown. He has married a Circassian slave, beautiful and healthy;

with her he has the odalisques, and if he chooses a slave of the harem who does not come under the title of odalisque, he would be obliged to instal her in a house apart— which would mean that the peace of the household would be compromised, and his own repose lost. Also the guardianship of the harems is wonderfully well carried out, and the virtue of a young woman is safer there than in any other form of life.

Then all the children are legitimate, and one of the most touching things in harem life is the love that all the women bear for the children of the master, even if they were born of a negress. As to the *Miss* or the *Mademoiselle*, I defy her to seduce the master or the son of the house.

CHAPTER II

HAVING said this, I will begin the true story of my life and adventures in the harem. I write English so badly that you must attribute the responsibility to a *Miss*, who flirted with the eunuchs young and old. She filled them with admiration with a series of high kicks to initiate them into the mysteries of the *cancan*.

Under the magnificent sway of Sultan Abdul Aziz in the year 1864, there came into the outskirts of the village of Stenia a little girl of four or five years old, led by a poverty-stricken old woman, who, going up to a boatman who was mending his *caïq*, proposed that he should look after the child whilst she entered the village to buy bread.

"You should give back the child to those you have stolen it from," said the boatman. "I shall take you to the Kadi if you do not at once tell me where you stole it."

"I swear to you I found this English girl on the road," said the woman stolidly, and she turned and, leaving the child, walked into the village.

"Machallah!" said the boatman, looking at the girl, "the rays of the sun are in your hair, and the velvet of Damascus in your eyes."

In a little while, as the woman did not return, Hussein the boatman ejaculated once more "Machallah!" and taking the little girl by the hand he led her to the village.

The child was dressed in a shabby garment of yellow silk trimmed with sable fur; on her head a gauze fichu embroidered with silk flowers, and on her feet little shoes with rose-coloured pompons.

" I am hungry," she said to Hussein.

He immediately bought her a cake, which she ate with avidity.

"You are an English girl, are you not, my lamb?" he asked.

The child said "Yes," and then "No."

Hussein had the idea that everything that was very fair and pink and white must have English blood in its veins, so thought the answer was "Yes."

With the delicacy innate amongst the Islamites he would not take the child into a Mussulman household; so he knocked at the door of a Christian, by name Cocona Elenco.

Like the greater part of the Greeks of Constantinople she was a gossip and liar; so had no hesitation in calling all the saints of her religion (and Allah knows how many Greek ones) to witness how great a marvel was the child.

"Ah! Kaïmeni, Kaïmeni," she repeated, "may the Blessed Virgin protect her! That beggar-woman has gone by—she will never come back."

And then, as nothing tends so much to solidify Greek friendship as little thefts, she took the gold thread embroidered handkerchief that was in the child's sash, and advised Hussein to take that lamb of God to some other roof than hers.

Hussein then led the child to the cottage of Doudou Artine, an Armenian woman, who lived by the sea. She received the girl with a smile, saying that they were already a large family, but would keep her. She offered her bread and olives, which the child ate with much appetite.

The cottage which Doudou and her girls inhabited was face to face with a mill belonging to a Frenchman, by name Pigeon, an extremely vulgar man but a good sort.

The Greek captains with black beards and fiery eyes brought the wheat for the mill, and girls used to glide languorously in front of the cottage, with their white veils folded back like the wings of tired birds.

It gave the virtuous daughters of Doudou a great deal of pleasure to watch the Greek captains, which was quite contrary to the projects of their mother. She held the Greek race in abhorrence, and in default of Armenians she would have preferred to see them marry Mussulmen. For Armenians and Turks, though differing in religion, have the same patriarchal tastes; and the father of a Turkish family, like that of an Armenian, is a model of devotion and goodness for his children. He likes a peaceful life, and is faithful to his creed, does not drink or gamble, and only finds pleasure amongst his own family.

From all times the Turks, recognising the quality of the Armenians, have given them posts of confidence. The best jewellers and agents are nearly always Armenians. Certain intriguers, members of the higher Armenian clergy, work hard to raise troubles in Armenia. It is said that they are paid by an European nation, but it is doubtful whether these adventurers, whose lives are long series of abominations, will succeed in their endeavours.

Doudou Artine, like the greater part of Armenian women, was of austere morals, for she had respect for fine traditions, and lived in the fear of evil, like the Mussulmen her neighbours.

Amongst these honest surroundings the little girl grew up, without their being able to conquer her wandering instincts. Doudou was very poor, and worked hard to keep her house together, whilst her daughters embroidered brilliant flowers on muslin handkerchiefs called *Yemeni*, which they sold for a livelihood.

But the child could never keep still long. She wandered into the streets where the Greek sailors drank *raki*. She jumped on the tables in front of wine shops—she sang—she danced—she kissed her hands to the rough sailors. She harangued them with pretty gestures, crying to them, "Ah, my fine captains with black beards and fiery eyes, what have you brought me back from your voyages?"

And the sailors, with their thick hair and strong necks and bright-coloured shirts, were delighted and laughed back, "My soul—my pretty little girl, here is what we have brought back from Odessa; we have not been further, come take them, they are for you," and they showered gilded sweetmeats on her, which were said to come from Paris. The child happy, and with sparkling eyes, accepted all as an offering that was due to her. She also had a very business-like friendship with a non-commissioned officer and the soldiers of the Ottoman Guard. She tyrannised over these brave soldiers, and her tyranny made itself heavily felt on their purse, for they received their pay very irregularly— but when the payment had been made a certain instinct seemed to warn her, and she claimed immediately her imperious desires. She wanted *mahalebi* or *friandises*, and the simple soldier paid for the caprices of this little pillaging soul. In the month of Ramazan she used to glide like an adder into the little low room where the humble *iftar* was laid out, the *hors-dœuvre* with which the fast was broken. At the first sound of the cannon which announced that the sun was set and the fast over for the day, she swallowed everything, and the slices of *pasterma* disappeared down her young greedy throat. The rough soldier, who could have easily crushed her like a fly between his strong fingers, looked at her with big stupid eyes, and said, "Machallah," (" Glory to God ").

On days when she was good, the child, who was now definitely called Ela, helped Artine Effendi to split open freshly-caught fish and spread them out in the sun, with a laurel leaf carefully placed under each.

When night came she slept on the floor
on a mattress beside Doudou, who kept
her warm and promised her cabbage and
rice on the morrow. But these morrows
became rare, and she thought more and
more of escaping to a neighbouring
village where an Egyptian Prince, whom
they said was rich and beautiful like the
Caliph Haroun-al-Raschid, had settled for
the winter.

This indomitable child—this capricious
Ela, was the author of this true story.
Many years have passed since these remembrances of childhood, but I still see
clearly those village streets, those little
cabarets where the Greek sailors used to
quarrel—the house of poor Doudou whom
in my unconscious cruelty I martyrised by
my caprices and ingratitude.

Weary of living in such poverty, I left
one day with Cocona Elenco, who was
going to sell scents in the harems of the
grand vizier Fuad Pasha. The grandson

of the Pasha noticed my pretty face, where sparkled eyes with a brightness surprising for my age. He brought me before the vizier, whom my gestures and manner much amused, and he promised that the family which had adopted me should be looked after; but I spoilt it all by saying to him, "Why do you have so ugly and old a wife? You would do better to marry me." That made every one laugh; and the son of the house, who spoke French fluently, said, "Cette petite ira loin, j'en donne ma parole!"

That was only a first incident without any consequences. Very soon I succeeded in penetrating, thanks to Cocona, into the harem of K—— Bey, who presented ambassadors. I created some little sensation, and they resolved to keep me as a playmate for the children of His Excellency. At the end of a week the eldest son of the Pasha took a fancy to me, and they sent me back to Doudou. I returned with my eyes full of tears and my arms filled with dresses given me by F—— Hanem, the eldest daughter of the Bey, a charming woman, who also was smitten with a desire to taste the education and life of Europeans. She went to pass a winter in Paris with a lady of the highest Parisian society, and returned with joy to the harem, much disillusioned on the subject of progress.

Doudou with deep sighs took me in her arms, and lifting her eyes to heaven said, "Lamb of God! you must have Circassian blood in your veins to wish so much to be sold." And I—I kissed her hands, begging her to sell me to the Palace, crying, "You will see, Doudou, I shall be Sultana, and you will be able to hang big emeralds in your ears and wear sables."

I did not then understand how much the poor Doudou loved me. I saw nothing of the beauty of the soul of those people, so honest, so good, who never lied or had an evil thought, and lived with peace amongst them.

CHAPTER III

BUT the day came when I resolutely escaped, and I returned no more to sing on the tables of the Greek wine-shops. I left those simple - minded men, with their hands rough from the ropes, with their curly hair on their fine heads, who deprived themselves of necessities to increase my childish amusements—I said to them quite simply, " Adieu, mes amis." And that was all. I went to find Hussein the boatman, and told him it was my heart's desire to go in his boat near the villa of the Egyptian Prince, and Hussein, who could refuse me nothing, took me.

The Prince and his suite were at that moment preparing to start in their six-oared boats as our *caïq* entered the little

gulf of Keurfesse.   Hussein passed respectfully at some distance, but I, quickly tearing
off my dress, tied a large gaily-coloured cloth
round me and jumped into the sea.   I could
swim like a flying fish, and whilst cleaving
the water, I promised a thousand presents
to poor horror-stricken Hussein.   " If the
Prince adopts me, you shall be my first
boatman," I cried to him.

I kept on swimming, my heart beating
violently in my breast, frozen by the cold.
The Prince and his suite watched with
curiosity this child that approached them,
and he asked me gently if I were not tired.

" No, since I see you, son of the King,"
I answered, blushing like a fine sunset.

" Help the child out of the water, and
bring her to me," ordered the Prince, who
then turned, and quickly entered the courtyard of the palace.

CHAPTER IV

"WHAT does Your Highness think of doing with his conquest from the bitter waves?" asked an old French gentleman, with the manners and appearance of a grand seigneur.

"You know what are my plans," answered the Prince. "The Armenians who found the child believe her to be English, and I shall leave her absolutely free till she is twenty-one. At that time, she shall choose for herself her manner of life and religion. Till then she will be in the harem, whence she can go out at her pleasure. I wish her to be free, strong, vigorous and independent."

"It is exile that gives you such republican ideas, Monseigneur," said the old Frenchman, smiling.

The Prince looked towards the Bosphorus, and shaking the ashes of his cigar into a silver cup placed by him on the sofa, said simply, " I hope to survive the pain of leaving Egypt and Choubra."

His cruel exile had already lasted six months, and suddenly losing all hope of its ceasing, the Prince was trying to create for himself a new existence. When he received at Cairo the imperative order to quit Egypt, he was not easily disposed to obey. He was the youngest son of Méhémet Ali, and the better part of Egypt belonged to him. His name was synonymous for power and grandeur ; the charm of his conversation, his love of sciences, of art and letters, which he protected as a generous Prince, had made him celebrated.

All illustrious men passing through Egypt begged the honour of being received at Choubra, and left enthusiastic with his reception of them.

Prince Halim was the type of the purest Bedouin race, with the perfect distinction of the oriental grand seigneur. His splendid eyes of striking beauty, his finely-cut nose with slender nostrils, his white teeth and brown moustache, his small arched foot, always booted by the best of London makers, made him a type of rare grace and elegance.

He spent royally his immense income, and Choubra being in the very heart of Egypt, the Viceroy Ismaël soon became uneasy of his being so near. Matters between the Prince and the Viceroy quickly became more than strained. Up till now Halim had always miraculously escaped the famous attempts against princely heirs.

From a bridge broken in advance by the orders of the Khedive, the train which was bringing all the princes invited to a Khedivial fête was hurled into the Nile. Not only did Halim save himself, but also seized from the jaws of death his favourite mameluke.

The Viceroy oppressed with taxes the people of the Prince, and he, wishing to make one last conciliatory effort towards his nephew Ismaël, offered him a fête at Choubra. It must be explained that the throne returning to the eldest of the princes of the Royal Family, Halim Pasha could only reign after the death of his nephew Ismael and of Prince Mustapha Fazil. This latter did not survive his exile.

At this fête at Choubra all the princes were invited with their harems. The most beautiful women of the kingdom found themselves together that evening.

The harem of Prince Halim was composed of five hundred women, all living in the palace.

There was the division of the Queen Dowager, the wife of the founder of the dynasty of Méhémet Ali, the division of the princesses, and that of each child of sufficient age to have a household.

These immense apartments were entirely distinct, each having their own slaves, eunuchs, baths, and carriages, making several houses in the same palace. The sitting-rooms were so vast that sometimes newly-bought little slaves lost their way and fell asleep in tears at the feet of immense silver candelabra, shaped like palms and arranged in avenues.

The princesses called on each other cere-moniously once or twice a month, being formally announced with rigid etiquette. The ladies of the palace had very formal ideas and magnificent manners, and rarely any close intimacy was known to exist. between the various divisions.

The following will give some idea of how the Prince lived at Choubra in the midst of his feminine world.

As to the princesses, the Prince visited them in their own apartments — and the women who have attained the rank of odalisques are on duty about his person in turn. Twelve of them do day duty for a week at a time, and these are then replaced by twelve more. Night duty is performed in the same way, but by one only for a week, who sleeps each night on a satin mattress across the doorway giving on the room of the Prince. What is peculiar is, that sometimes this guard is kept by some slave who is not popular with the Prince, but each one who has been bought for this service has the right of eight days' guard, and the master submits to this order of things. The week of duty of each of these ladies is arranged with regard to their state of health. They take their baths regularly, and four or five hours is not considered too long for beautifying purposes.

When one of them becomes a mother, she does not appear for a whole year before the Prince after the birth of the child. If

she gives birth to a boy, she takes the title
of Oumil Bey, or should it be a daughter,
she is called ever afterwards Ouma Hariem.
And the new state in the household arouses
no hatred or jealousy, all the children being
legitimate. The same customs are observed
in the palaces of the Sultan and Imperial
Princes.

CHAPTER V

THE Prince had decided that the fête given in honour of the Khedive should take place in the division of the palace where the Vice-Queen Dowager, his mother, lived.

The widow of Méhémet Ali was still imposing and beautiful, and had the grand air of an autocratic sovereign, and Ismaël never felt quite at his ease in her presence. She was widow of the chief of the dynasty, and blamed the Khedive openly for his tyranny towards the fellahs, and warned him repeatedly of the inevitable difficulties which the disorder of his government would bring.

The day before the fête, the first lady of the household, who always arranged the functions, summoned the treasure-keepers, those who brought coffee, and chibouk-bearers, the singers and musicians and waiting-servants, and the role of each group was carefully made out according to custom. The eunuchs (important personages—for they are the sole intermediaries between the harems and outside life) walked watchfully about the apartments. They looked on at all these preparations, smiling and making fun of the airs and graces of the women. The chief of them, Billal Agha, looked carefully after the jewels, and was much exercised in his mind as to whether he ought to receive the Vice-Queen on the second or third step of the grand staircase. The fear of possible exile for his Prince inspired a new humility in this proud man. The chief eunuch of the Imperial Palace has a rank equivalent to that of a grand vizier, and all ministers are doubtful and a little afraid of his intrigues. In forty or fifty years they will

no longer fear them, as there will be no
more eunuchs, not even in the Sultan's
court, for it is a luxury which is already
beginning to pass away.

The women, ready for the part they are
to play, group themselves in the apartment
of the Queen Dowager.   The musicians
tune their instruments, whilst the leader
of the orchestra, a beautiful Circassian
woman aged twenty-five, tells them the
names of the pieces that are to be played.
The musical memory amongst Turkish
women is remarkable, and they can easily
reproduce any piece they have heard three
or four times ; but an European professor,
who would teach them according to his
methods, would never succeed in making
anything of them, and they are best left
to their primitive methods and to their
natural gift.   The chibouk-bearers fill the
pipes with amber mouth-pieces, covered
with jewels.   Those that are studded
with big rubies are to be presented

to the Viceroy and Vice-Queens, and
those with diamonds to the Princes and
Princesses of the second rank.

The salvers on which were carried the
long chibouks were of marvellous beauty.
On each was a representation of a garden ;
in the centre stood a palm-tree, round which
twined a snake in emeralds and diamonds,
the dates on the palm being rubies, and
at the base of the palm there glittered a
stream of diamonds. Amongst the treasures
of the Prince there were twelve of these
dishes.

Already the chibouk-bearers, according
to their rank, followed each other, preceded
by a eunuch who made a way through
the crowd of slaves. The coffee-bearers
arranged their silk cloths embroidered with
pearls and gold and diamond dust, and
their gold trays thickly studded with
sapphires. Each cup placed on one of
these trays must be carried a distance of
at least thirty paces without spilling a drop.

The dancers bent themselves backwards as low as possible, giving their whole bodies a little tremulous movement.   All the jewels of the treasury were scattered over them, and they looked like living flowers.

The singing women were silent, with the idea of strengthening their contralto voices. They were dressed in pure white, shot with silver thread, and on their bare necks wore strings of fine pearls.   Over their hair they had white tarlatan veils embroidered with jasmine.

One by one the great silver palm-trees were lit up, and at the base of the white marble columns one could see the pious slaves at prayer on their orange velvet carpets.   The immense fountain gave a gentle murmur with the water that flowed into it from mouths of marble lions and strings of amber chained silver goblets to the jaws of the lions, where young slaves came and drank furtively, looking with large eyes at their own reflection in the fountain. A long day passed in the bath having given a new freshness to their satin skins; and their eyes, carefully enlarged with *rastec* and *sarmé*, sparkled with extraordinary brightness. The fear of making some slight error in presenting the coffee to the princes, made them tremble slightly.

Suddenly a eunuch passed close to them crying "*Destour !*" "*Destour !*" ("attention"), and then twenty or thirty eunuchs followed running and uttering the same cry, and the slaves drew themselves up in line, with their arms crossed on their breasts.

The *sais*, the runners of the Vice-Queens, stopped abruptly at the foot of the grand staircase, their resin torches covering the façade of the palace with a purple glow. One heard the noise of their heavy breathing, and one of them, with his mouth open, with mad eyes and convulsed face, fell fainting; he was quickly carried away, and a stain of blood was on the floor.

Crushed with the weight of their jewels,

the Vice-Queens, supported by the eunuchs, made their entry into the *Salle des Fêtes*. The first twelve women were wearing the finest jewels of the treasury, and wore high white satin boots, each button of which was a large single diamond—a detail when being later reported to the Sultan, he decided to increase the taxation he had already imposed on the Viceroy of Egypt.

Ismaël escorted by the princes then came, and the women's orchestra received him with a beautifully played piece, followed by the songs of the Arab and Turkish singers.

Dinner was announced by twenty-four young women with gold - embroidered napkins on their arms, and served French fashion. On the table were massive gold centre-pieces set with jewels, and the slaves, with their long hair down their backs and bare shoulders served the feast.

Prince Halim, who was decidedly a

gourmet, had a famous French chef called Bernard, who on this occasion surpassed himself. Everything was perfectly carried out, and dinner was prolonged slightly beyond the limits prescribed by etiquette.

The illuminations in the gardens of Choubra for a short time amused the Khedive, who showed considerable impatience to see a young Circassian dancing-girl called Cehere, whom it was said Prince Halim had recently bought.

She was to dance for the first time, and though she was not exactly pretty she had a great charm about her. She had many hopes of pleasing the Khedive, and thought that if this were so, her master would offer her as a present to Ismaël. She entered the *Salle du Divan* in charge of a eunuch, who pointed out to her the Khedive, the princes and princesses who were in the centre of a brilliant circle. She stood still, apparently both agitated and nervous for a moment, and everyone looked at her with considerable curiosity, her breast rising and falling tumultuously, making the sequins and jewels with which she was covered sparkle in the light. Suddenly her eyes lit up, and shaking her shoulders, she advanced with the undulating movement of a snake to the very feet of the Khedive, and throwing her body backwards with wonderful grace, she inundated the carpet with her beautiful hair, which floated out and sank round her like a shadow.

Ismaël let fall the ashes of his cigar into the silver cup, and looking fixedly at the dancer, said to her, "*Afferim kez*" ("brave girl"), which surprised every one.

She raised herself slowly and danced gradually further away with wonderful undulations, sometimes letting her head rest on her shoulder, and with gestures that seemed to say "Come—follow me!"

Suddenly she stopped, and with a quick movement on her castanets, she fled with all the lightness of a gazelle. In an instant

she was back again, dancing feverishly with an ever increasing movement, which had a great effect on the onlooking princes, who all, as a sign of admiration, drew their fezes lower over their eyes.

But what was fated was bound to happen, and the truth is that Cehere—who was exerting herself to her best that she might be given as a present to the Khedive—was, at the same time, examining her master, Prince Halim, with curiosity, whom till this moment she had never seen; and, with the real Circassian temperament, she instantly changed her mind, and was quite convinced that she had fallen madly in love with him. These sudden passions, which are not uncommon amongst Turkish women, often change their ambitious dreams into quite modest realities. It was otherwise with Cehere, who was unable to realise her passionate caprice, for she had captivated the Khedive, and the Prince begged him to accept her; and being hastily covered with a blue silk *haick*, was taken off to the Khedive's palace.

The dancer thus given over to the service of the Khedive, took from the moment of her entry into the harem her turn of night duty. But she swore to herself that she would resist as much as possible this man whom she did not love, little thinking that unconsciously she was deciding the exile of the Prince for whom she had conceived so great a passion.

To the first questions put to her by Ismael, who was inspired by a great fancy for her, she answered that she could never love any other man than Prince Halim.

This annoyed the Khedive, and this jealousy, added to a good many former ones, resulted in a thousand vexatious acts against the Prince, to which one day he answered by a letter which has since become famous.

The next day he was forced to quit Choubra and become an exile, leaving behind him his mother, his children, and their mothers, and a legitimate wife to whom he was devoted.

Ismaël behaved infamously to those poor women, who in their misery only wished to die. He gave orders that the bare necessaries of life should be denied them. The mother of the Prince died, killed more by sorrow than privations, and before death prophesied the future exile of the persecutor of her son.

On disembarking at Constantinople the Prince installed himself in a house at Stamboul, which house, thanks to the persistent anger of the Khedive, took fire. But the Prince and his suite escaped this third generous attempt of Ismaël. They were then obliged to seek a palace big enough to lodge the Egyptian Prince, and that of Keurfesse was chosen.

The impossibility of ruining the Prince made the Khedive a little more reasonable, and by degrees things arranged themselves in Egypt. A *soi-disant* polish Prince, a spy in the pay of Ismaël, attached to the person of Prince Halim, persuaded him that it were better to renounce all idea of returning to Cairo, and to accept an income of sixty thousand pounds a year which Egypt agreed to pay.

The loss of his Choubra property was the most cruel blow to the Prince, and he hesitated for a long time in accepting the proposition. At last the Khedive had the pleasure of seeing the affair terminate in the way he wished, and he presented the Pole with one hundred and twenty thousand pounds as *backseesh*.

A crowd of slaves and mamelukes therefore left Choubra, some of them joining their master in his palace in Stamboul, and others going to establish themselves in a palace in Cairo, inhabitated by a divorced wife of the Prince, but for whom he still kept up an establishment.

When the royal yacht which brought the eldest daughter of the Prince, followed by all those who had the happiness to share the exile of their master, dropped anchor in the little gulf, the band on board played the Egyptian March, which brought tears to the eyes of the master and the slaves.

The unhappy Princess, whose beauty, elegance, and generosity were proverbial throughout Egypt, notwithstanding her great pride, could not play the part of a sovereign on leaving the ship, and cried like the humblest fellahine.

This disembarkation of the entire harem and the immense cases containing the clothes and treasures was a curious sight; it lasted three days.

CHAPTER VI

FOR a whole week the palace of Keurfesse resounded with cries, tears and oaths of vengeance from the women of the harem. They found themselves very uncomfortable, for the place was only furnished after the Turkish ideas, and they much missed all the luxury of Choubra.

Accustomed as they were to soft rich carpets, here the floors were covered with matting the colour of ripe wheat, and the sofas miserably furnished in faded cretonnes, and thin white curtains to the windows. Their teeth chattered with cold, and they rolled themselves up in woollen coverings, walking up and down the large corridors to try to keep warm. Also they suffered a good deal from the change of climate.

The eunuchs superintended the installation with a sad air, employing Armenian servants. They, being new, offered at least some slight distraction to the women, who amused themselves watching them.

These servants are generally fine men, and in rich households are magnificently dressed in embroidered garments, with beautiful cashmere shawls round their waists. Round their necks, which are bare, are massive silver chains, to which are attached watches in several tortoise-shell cases. It is a fine sight to see them enter the harem with large dishes on their heads, with high metal coverings, and a purple silk cloth thrown over the whole. As they walk in in single file, they have the appearance of gigantic poppies.

. . . .

The Prince had in his service the in-evitable *Miss*, who taught French and English to the children and those of the slaves who merited this distinction. I was one of these, and Miss B——— owned that I was intelligent, but intractable. Nevertheless I profited considerably from her lessons.

I was never far from the Prince, and from the first moment attached myself to his footsteps, always ready to hand him cigarettes, and offering to run on commissions for him. If I were absent long, he invariably sent for me, making me sit beside him on the sofa, and taking my face between his hands he would kiss me and wind my long yellow hair round his neck.

"Where have you been, my child?" he would say gently. "Some day some brigand will steal you when you go through the bazaars and are out of sight of the slaves."

"Never," I answered, "for everyone knows me and loves me, and they like me to please you, for they know that later I shall be your wife, and you will be King of Egypt."

He smiled gently and patted my head with his slender fingers, whilst I could not take my eyes off him—the eyes already of a woman who loves.

Nevertheless that insatiable desire for wandering was strong in me, and, followed at a distance by a slave, I visited the harems of all the great personages; and having a reputation for being amusing and pleasant, I was welcomed everywhere. Sometimes I danced for the poor boatmen, and on leaving them, I would enter the harem of Cheik ul Islam, and pray with the fanatical old ladies who read the Koran without understanding it. During the Ramazan I would break the fast, sometimes with an aide-de-camp of His Majesty, sometimes with the wife of a poverty-stricken fisherman. Or I followed the funeral of a Greek who was being carried to the grave with an uncovered face; or guided by Cocona Elenco, I would go with her and drink the water of a sacred spring of the Blessed Virgin. On entering the palace I would glide into the priest's

chamber and await the hour for the summoning of prayer. How beautiful he was,
that singing priest, with his Indian muslin
turban, white as the snow on the mountains!
He was an Arab from Hedjaz, of pure race,
and on seeing him pass, the women looking
at him through the gratings would become
pale with emotion. When, wrapped in his
white linen cloak and wearing a black
caftan, he walked along the front of the
palace chanting "*Allah u Ekber*," and calling
the faithful to prayer, there was an absolute
silence; for Mussulmen and Christians alike
were moved by that voice, for its sweetness
and caressing charm surpassed all other
music. The Prince himself would forget
his dreamings and listen with delight, and
would say to those near him, "Ah! if the
celebrated Patti had heard Mollah Izzedin,
she would understand what a human voice
really was, and would never sing another
note herself."

Being on terms of great intimacy with

the Minister of War and his harem, I
came back one day with the present of a
small carbine, and I asked the Prince that
I might be taught how to use it. He
sent me up to the top of a neighbouring
hill, under the charge of an *aïvasse* and
two eunuchs. There I found Demir Aga
Couroudje, the agent of the property, sitting
on a carpet. Demir Aga was a hero who
had been in many engagements, having
originally been a leader of a band of
brigands, and bore in his body several
bullets, and many a wound on his face.
Demir Aga had very magnificent manners,
and was fond of recounting interminable
stories of his father's doings, who had been
a Greek by birth. He himself had become
a Mussulman in his youth, and the only
custom he had retained of a Greek brigand
was the relieving of passers-by of their purses.
But since he had entered the service of the
Prince, he contented himself with guarding
the property instead of attacking.

To reach him we were obliged to follow a long path edged with cypresses, and the eunuchs became much alarmed.

" Ela Hanem, our lamb," they said trembling, " what will become of us if this brigand should become angry ? "

" I have no fear, my lions," I answered, " you will see he will receive us well."

As a point of fact with a certain dignity he told the eunuchs to tell the Prince that he would carefully watch over the child. "On my head, I will be answerable for her," he added.

Nevertheless they were ill at ease, and hurried back down the hill, having made him innumerable profound bows.

" My child," said the old hero, fixing me with his eagle eye, " you have beautiful golden hair, and velvety eyes."

I sat down close to him on the carpet, on which were laid out symmetrically, on his right, his pipe, his arms and various necessaries, whilst on his left on the turf were his shoes. A magnificent umbrella pine shadowed us, and all round us were still larger trees, which somewhat softened the rays of the sun.

The Bosphorus lay stretched out at the foot of the hill, and I watched the old man, who recounted to me a long story, to which I fear I did not listen much. He passed his hand over his eyes, murmuring "Machallah"; and evening came slowly, covering the ground with its long shadows, and the grey wings of the little bats fluttered in the mystery and silence of the growing night.

The old man had a tender heart, and seeing that I was saddened, he spread a napkin over my knees, and opening a covered dish, he took a *dolma* and put it in my mouth, and then with little bits of bread gently wiped the oil from the corners of my lips, saying: "You see how you please my soul since I give you *becquee* with my own hand. Don't cry, little one, do as the birds do over our heads, cover yourself and sleep."

He combed my hair with a six-toothed comb, and then wrapping me up in a sheep-skin laid me down on the carpet. But the stars which sparkled in the sky seemed so extraordinarily brilliant that night, that I pointed them out to the brigand. He seemed indifferent, and only answered, "My lamb, it is time to sleep."

He sat near me and began singing to send me to sleep. His song was on five notes only, and was in praise of his own brilliant fighting. He had arrived at the point of describing the tenth head he had cut off, when I said to him, "My father, I am asleep."

When the sun was up, I awoke and found before me, laid out on a fig leaf, a cake and three black olives, which I ate. Then the cleansing operations took some time. First of all the carpet had to be thoroughly brushed, the stockings were washed, and the night-coverings shaken out and rolled round a piece of wood, and feet, hands, ears and nostrils, all washed whilst muttering religious sentences.

The rest of the day was spent in doing nothing and sitting still without moving. Why, indeed, agitate oneself when one has nothing to say or do. That is what is called *kief*.

Like the preceding night, I had to listen to the song about the heads that were cut off, one of which it seems began to move its eyes after decapitation, which offended the Aga — it was the head of a Greek—whereupon the Aga told it that if it continued to open and shut its eyes, he would cut out its tongue, and this threat had the effect of making the eyes close once and for all.

The next day I said softly to the Aga, " Sir brigand, I am beginning to be bored, please conduct me back to the Palace."

So I walked down the hill followed by the Aga, who had put on his most magnificent clothes and made a very fine appearance. On leaving him he called down on me Allah's blessing, and I kissed his hand, as is the custom to do when with those who teach you.

CHAPTER VII

AS time went on, a more or less super-ficial reconciliation was effected be-tween Prince Halim and the Khedive Ismaël, and amicable relations were renewed between the harems of Egypt and those of the exile, though Halim still continued to live at the palace of Keurfesse. The new situation affected me considerably, for it brought me in contact with the Khedive and his wives.

Ismaël begged the Prince to allow me to go and stay with his daughter Princess Fatma, which new plan did not please me at all, nor could I hide my dislike to the idea. I sought the Prince, and kissing his hands, said, "As I am obliged to go, let me at least pass this last day near you."

That day Halim was engaged in having the diamonds of his treasury washed, and himself assisted at the delicate operation, which consisted in soaking the jewels in a kind of acid which loosened them from their settings. With a child's pleasure I plunged my hands in the basins, letting the glittering diamonds run through my fingers.

When they were washed, they were put into bags carefully arranged on the table. I emptied them into my hands, which were too small to hold their shining contents, and many were scattered on the carpet. It amused the Prince, and he drew me towards him, pressing my cheek against his, and with his wonderfully young laugh he said, "I am twenty years older than you, my child, but I wait with impatience till you are twenty-one, when I shall marry you. Do you understand that?"

Certainly I understood, and a shiver made my lips whiten, and my eyelids close.

Was it possible, he thought, that a young

girl could, without knowing it, love him, in the same way in which he loved her?

He rose and walked to the window, over the white bearskins which covered the floor of the room.

"Ela," he said, "Come," and holding me in his arms he covered my eyes and cheeks with quick, passionate kisses. "I love you," he said, "I love you."

. . . .

I stayed three days with Princess Fatma, the daughter of the Khedive. She was the most haughty of all the Princesses, and wished to dazzle me, so that on my return the harem of Prince Hamil should receive from me a detailed account of the extraordinary *luxe* that surrounded her.

On my arrival at the Khedivial palace, the ladies' maids undressed me and led me to the Turkish bath, then clothed me in the most wonderful gold-embroidered silks, trimmed with *point d'Alençon* and English lace, shoes with gold heels, strings of emeralds, rings on every finger, diamond flowers in my hair and four rows of diamonds round my neck.

Decked out in this manner I was led into the presence of the Princess, who received me with a chill dignity of manner, and gave me her hand to kiss.

The apartments of the Princess were given up to great disorder, and luxury was allowed to run riot, which greatly spoilt the general effect. All that woman's extravagant imagination could conceive was realized to an absurd extent. From Paris, from China, Stamboul, and America, were brought clothes and jewels. Worth sent dresses; the jewellers, masses of rings, necklaces and bracelets.

Every day came singers and dancers and rows of slaves. The Princess herself examined them, saying to one : " Show me your teeth." To another : " Let me see your back—or your shoulders." Quantities of these girls were bought, many of whom were almost ill with emotion and delight at finding themselves chosen for royal service. The governesses were enriched with a thousand things that the princesses were tired of. Almost daily some caprice or other sent a French servant to Paris or elsewhere for some trivial purpose, such as to get a tooth-brush!

And nothing would have induced the Princess Fatma to use any brush but the one brought from Paris by the servant who had been sent solely for this important commission.

This special envoy always travelled first-class, smoked enormous and expensive cigars, and dazzled the shops that supplied the royal household, with his descriptions. Alas! these descriptions were in no way exaggerated. The French chef did his work in the kitchens in sleeves of Valenciennes lace. And the house steward gave wonderful fêtes, to which all the merchants of Pera were invited. He royally spent the Egyptian money, saying grandly,

c

" We will show them what it is to enter-
tain." The ladies' maids wore dresses from
Worth, saying, " It is the Princess who
pays, but it is we who wear these
clothes."

Like all the Princes of his house, Ismaël
had the gift of inspiring great affection
amongst the women of his harem; and
many of them were consumed with love
for him, which was all the more extraordinary, for he was fat, and heavy and
unattractive. Nevertheless, he had a certain
charm about him.

As to Prince Halim, he was really irresistible, but at least he had the most
beautiful eyes; and the most lovely
courtezans would have gladly thrown over
the Khedive himself for a flower that he
had worn. And at Constantinople, when
he passed in his beautiful boat with his
ten rowers, many a shutter opened and
flowers were thrown towards him.

One evening the Khedive sent for me.

I found him sitting on his sofa wrapped in a long fur garment. He had taken off his European clothes, and his bare feet, having been bathed in rose-water, were curled up under him. He looked at me fixedly for a moment, and then asked me to light him a cigarette, adding almost roughly, " Do you do the same for the Prince?"

I said " Yes."

"If you like you shall marry my son Mehmet Twefik—you please me."

"Thank you," I answered, "I do not care about young men."

"Very well then, if you wish it, you shall be the prettiest of the Vice-Queens."

"Again I must thank you Highness, but it is the Prince my master who pleases me."

" Machallah!" cried Ismaël, " he fascinates you all from your cradles. You will return to your lover, and you will tell him from me that the *irade* changing the succession to the throne of Egypt is really signed at last.

Go—it is a piece of news that will give him pleasure ; for the future, it will be enough for him to reign in your hearts. You may return to him."

A governess was called, who re-conducted me to the Prince, but the affair was carried out with considerable formality. Two eunuchs followed us, bearing the clothes and jewels the Vice-Queen had given me, and Ismaël ordered that the little steam-launch that had brought me should be left as a remembrance of my visit to him.

One may imagine how glad I was to leave the palace where, the day before, I had seen little slaves weeping into gold cups, where the tears were preserved for bathing the cheeks of the Princess, with the idea that it would bring back the natural colour. At the last moment Ismaël called me to him, and embraced me several times saying—

"You will come again to Egypt, will you

not, to see me and my daughter, Princess Fatma. She is very delicate, and this warm sun is necessary for her."

In truth, this poor princess had that strange beauty which is not uncommon amongst those who die young. She was always dressed in long dresses of some rare delicate stuff of a dazzling white, and her short, Venetian-red hair made the delicacy and paleness of her neck and face the more remarkable. Her almond-shaped eyes seemed weary and half-veiled with the immensely long eye-lashes.

All the great ladies that were admitted to her presence left very much impressed with her unusual and mysterious beauty.

She died soon afterwards, and two days after her death, as is the custom, were given up to the lamentations of the crying women, who remained in a room close at hand, where all the women of the harem came and cried in their turn.

Her slaves were dowered and married off

according to their rank; for rich Turks always give devoted slaves their freedom by marriage, and dower them sufficiently to live comfortably afterwards. That is why Circassian girls who know this custom prefer to be sold at Stamboul than to live in Circassia, where no such good fortune could happen to them. They beg their fathers or brothers to sell them, and this slavery will always exist as long as there are rich men in Turkey; and the most anxious to keep up this custom are the slaves themselves, who prefer to tempt the fortune of the unknown, to live in privation and rough labour in their own country. If the girl is beautiful she becomes a success, and if ugly, a slave in a more ordinary harem, where she is seldom ill-treated. The slow indifference of the Turkish nature makes service easy, and the master looks carefully after the health of his slaves. The mutual feeling of live and let live is a prevailing one in harems;

the women are fond of the master, and value the legitimacy of the children.

In all harems there is a great deal of politeness and complimentary speeches amongst the women. There are no jealousies, and rarely quarrels, but seldom great friendships. Each of the ladies is anxious to impress the others with the fact that she has been well educated, and most succeed in cultivating a certain charm of manner, which helps to make the interior life of Islamite homes agreeable and pleasant. The children are respectful to their parents, and never speak to them unless they are first spoken to. When the "Mademoiselle" or "Miss" try to break through the custom, they seldom succeed in their work of so-called civilisation.

When I was fifteen years old, if I went out I was always dressed as a European, and considered as being of English birth. When a Turk marries a Christian, she is nearly always free to go out as she likes, and do as did the wives of Nedjib Pasha and Suavi Pasha, who when paying visits to Europeans, always dressed as French-women, or paying visits to Turkish ladies, were clothed like Eastern women.

My somewhat precocious intelligence made every one kind to, and confidential with, me. They knew at heart I was Islamite, if not by birth, and the certainty that on reaching the age of twenty-one I should embrace their religion made me sympathetic to them. They loved me for a sort of charm which they expressed by the word "*Chirinelik*," and if any little differences arose, they always said, "Go, my lamb, and settle that business; you have a way with you which no one can resist."

At the house of Hussein Avni (the Minister of War) I was treated always as a daughter of the family, and I was the only one who was able to obtain permission from him for a dress from Paris for his child.

At my first arrival the wife of the Minister said to me : "Go and find the Pasha, for my daughter's heart is aching for a dress from Madame Soinard, and you know he is very severe, and does not like French dresses. Go, my little lioness, and try to get leave from him, and I will make you a present of a beautifully embroidered hand-kerchief."

I immediately entered his office, where there was a perpetual coming and going of aides-de-camp, and where, notwithstanding his serious occupations, he received me in an affectionate and paternal manner.

"Ah! Ela Hanem," he said, "I see clearly that my wife wants something, for when I was in the harem she did nothing but tell me of the things she and our daughter wanted; and now she makes you follow me to the office. It is unreasonable. I am the poorest of all the Ministers; I don't know how to steal money from my country. Tell the women that I have none."

Alas! this was only too true, but like all Turks, he had a great devotion to his children, and could refuse nothing to his daughter.

She (rather maliciously, when he would not immediately gratify her wish) always ran away, and would not let him kiss her which spoilt the whole day for the poor father.

Hussein Avni was the bravest, cleverest and best of the generals, and the Sultan Abdul Aziz, in his heart of hearts knew it, and if he sometimes placed the general in disgrace, he soon recalled him. He was a fine soldier, of which he had given proofs on many occasions. His advice was generally considered the best, and nearly always followed in military counsels. Charming to those he loved, his generosity was greater than his means; remarkably intelligent, he spoke French like a native, a talent he generally himself ignored. His bravery was well known, and he had quelled many a revolt by the seduction of his speech and his persuasiveness and conciliatory manner to his enemies.

His harem was on very simple lines; even his women were seldom dressed in silk, and went out very little, and the old-fashioned Mussulman austerity was practised in his household. No governesses had ever been allowed to bring trouble there, and two of his children (who were from the age of seven brought up for entering a religious order) and Hairiee Hanem were educated *à la turque*.

Two things amongst others were remarkable in that house: one was his beautiful collection of arms, and the other, the correct behaviour of his aides-de-camp, whom he chose and formed with much care. One of them, by name Hassan, a Circassian, became the type of extreme military elegance; on him the Minister showered kindnesses and treated as his own son.

But Hassan, whose distinguished and martial appearance had attracted the attention of the Sultan, was appointed in attendance on His Imperial Highness Youssouf Izzedin, the eldest son of His Majesty.   His appointment was much regretted by Hussein Avni, who had considered him as devoted entirely to himself.

It was when she was about sixteen that Hairiee Hanem, the daughter of the Minister for War, was suddenly seized with a passion for dress. The visits that she paid or received made her discontented and envious of the jewels, dresses and luxury of her friends, and in the evening when her father came, worn out and harassed with the insurmountable difficulties in raising the money necessary for the wants of the army, he would find Hairiee fretful and disinclined for the paternal embrace.

He adored his child, and would have committed a crime to save her from tears ;

so he generally finished in giving in to her caprices.

The Minister was a thorough patriot, honest and loyal, and without doubt was the only one who had not enriched himself at the expense of the state. These desires of his daughter astonished him, but he had not the time to try and understand them, occupied as he was entirely with his work. Summoned perpetually before the Sultan, he was on his feet from four o'clock in the morning, and the anguish of seeing everything going wrong by the fault of his master the Sultan, whose phenomenal expenses plunged the Empire in difficulties, made his existence almost insupportable.

He tried by every means to respectfully explain to the Sultan how the army was situated—that army of which he might indeed be proud, with its sublime devotion and great moral and physical force.

Occasionally Abdul Aziz would pull himself up, but like the great child that he was would soon fall again in the same hopeless fashion.

Little by little the Minister gave up the idea of telling the Sultan how things were; and by degrees a group of students formed themselves into a band of malcontents, and one day organised a manifestation in front of the palace.

The Sultan sent them money, and the manifestation passed off. This affair ought to have awakened the attention of His Majesty, for he was already sufficiently astonished that the students had the audacity to assemble at his very gates; but what was fated was bound to come to pass.

CHAPTER VIII

ONE day I had gone to the Minister for War to tell him of a new desire of Hairiee's, when he begged me to be the bearer myself of a letter to the Prince Halim.

" I advise you not to lose it," he said as he gave it me, and I felt a sort of tremor as I met his eyes.

When I reached the palace they told me the Prince was absent. With a sadness that I could not explain I sat down. and my slave, having waited some time in front of me with crossed arms, seeing that I asked for nothing, retired silently. I took my guitar and began playing almost unconsciously, watching meanwhile through the open windows the boats floating on the calm waters of the Bosphorus.

A great silence lay over the sea, and a delicious fragrance on the evening air, but somehow I could not shake off the vague feeling of melancholy which oppressed me.

The sudden rush of oars through the water made me lean out, and I saw the *caïq* of the Prince glide up along the landing-stage, and stop suddenly at the white marble steps with a sureness and precision which is a great art amongst the boatmen.

All the blood in my heart seemed to surge up to my head. I drew a hand-mirror from the cushions of the divan, and looked at myself critically; then quickly passing between my eyelids a tortoise-shell pin, arranged the folds of my rose-coloured *ïntari*, and slipped on my slippers which I had left at the foot of the divan, felt for the letter which I had hidden in my breast, and then I went out.

I was obliged to pass right through the harem. It was the hour for food, and the

slaves were passing with large covered
silver dishes on their 'heads, whilst the
eunuch who was on duty called repeatedly
" *Destour !* " (" attention "). On all sides I
heard the light laughter of the women,
who were playing *tric-trac*, which was the
last new game in the harem, and which,
like all other games, had its short reign
and then vanished. I passed through the
long bare corridors, where a soft, warm
wind floated in through the open doors,
and up the matting-covered stairs, and past
the big room reserved for the children who
were being taught to sing the Koran, and
crossing the garden I went towards the
kiosque which the Prince had had built,
and which he only quitted in the great
heat of summer.

The slaves on duty were sitting in a
large circle on the ground, awaiting the
arrival of the Prince, who had not yet
come in. I sat down on one of the
violet satin divans, and listened to the

adventures of Nasreddin Hodja, that a
lady secretary was reading aloud to the
women. One of them respectfully begged
the reader if she would stop the reading,
and write a letter for her to her sister,
who was one of the coffee-bearers to the
Khedive. The secretary drew from her
sash the case containing the Chinese ink
and a pen, and immediately wrote down
the long list of compliments which it is
the custom to begin a letter with, and
then asked the girl if there were anything
she particularly wished to say.

" No," said the slave, " so long as it is
a letter ; that is all I wish to send her."

The whole group was much interested
in the letter, which, when finished, was
handed to a eunuch, who passed it on to
a messenger, who in his turn gave it to
another of lower degree, who put it in
the folds of his sash — the invariable
destiny of the rare letters that were
written in the harem.

The Prince entered, and two slaves immediately preceded His Highness to the entrance of his room, where they stood before the door which he left half open behind him. I glided into the room, and Halim turning swiftly round, threw his arms about me and kissed my eyes, holding me in a close embrace. On hearing the steps of two slaves who were on duty approaching, he went and sat down, and asked for a cigar from one of them. I then drew from my dress the letter of the Minister of War, and laid it on his knees, feeling not unmoved, as I always did, in his presence. He read it through several times, whilst the slaves, bearing heavy silver torches stood near him, holding their burdens first in one hand, and then in the other, for their weight was so great that it made them tremble.

Suddenly he held the letter to one of the flames and watched it slowly burn.

"There was enough in it to cause one to

be taken to the Place d'Acq Meiden" (the place of execution), he said to me in French, in a voice so shaken by emotion that I felt as if I had suddenly received a wound.

 .   .   .   .   .   .

The next day I was summoned to the presence of His Highness, who gave me a small bag of grey cloth tied with string and sealed with red wax.

"You must take this to the harem of the Minister of War. To-day being Friday, he will go out very late, you will give it him with your own hands," he said.

On arriving at the house, I was so early that the Minister received me with a fur cloak thrown over his sleeping-clothes, and who cried when he saw me, " Thanks be to Allah! what news?"

Whilst his wife said : "Well, my child, the flowers are still red with the dawn, and you are already here."

"Don't talk, my wife," said he, "but order some fruits for the child," and then he examined closely the seals on the package.

"More surprises from Paris?" she asked. "What is there in the bag—money?—or some new French inventions?—tell me, Pasha, what is it?"

Then understanding that she would learn nothing, she laughed, the rather loud laugh of a somewhat vulgar woman.

Hussein Avni had married her when he was a *sous-officier*, and since that time he had never even dreamt of making her unhappy by choosing another and perhaps more refined wife.

Two slaves brought in a Roman salad, cherries, strawberries, cooked beans, and boiled maize, which we all three tranquilly ate with all the enjoyment of real Turks, for these plain repasts are much appreciated by the simple-minded Mussulman. The Minister was much amused at the way his wife teased me with a hundred questions, and naturally taking advantage of my presence, led the conversation on to the subject of dresses from Paris, pretending to hesitate concerning the respective merits of Laferrière and Soinard.

Suddenly the Minister said to me with a kindly smile: " Ela, my child, write to Laferrière to send a dress for my child, only write quickly, my lamb."

"Certainly," I answered, "only you must bear in mind that she is more expensive than Soinard."

"But much more *chic*," interrupted Madame Hussein Avni, and at the use of this French word we all laughed.

"You may write," said the Pasha. " I will pay, for the Sultan is very generous to me— and at this moment, when I am Grand Vizier and Minister of War, everything is in my hands; there is nothing that I need refuse, and I shall do as others do. Fortune at last opens the door that I had double-locked. An honest man !—what is that ? No one believes or gives one credit for being it. Hitherto I have deprived Hairiee of many things ;

now she shall have all she wishes—nothing shall be too good or expensive for her. *Allons!* Hairiee, my sweet-eyed one, my treasure," he continued, laying aside his chibouk and drawing towards him this ungrateful child, who was later to cause him such great misfortunes, "what do you wish now?—what is the desire of your heart?"

She only smiled, and as the Minister was now due at the War Office, he put on his coat, and whilst the slaves were drawing on his boots, his wife seized this unexpected opportunity to give him a list of all the things he was to buy in the town — a ruby and diamond tiara for Hairiee—who was going to the wedding of one of the ladies of the palace — a *coupé* with English horses for their son, a hundred pieces of Indian muslin for their slaves, six Japanese dishes big enough to hold a roast sheep, white tortoise-shell spoons, and innumerable packets of wax candles.

The Pasha listened patiently. He had always done the commissions for his wife, and he had no idea of changing the customs of his life, which was entirely sacrificed to the happiness of his family. Then looking at the clock, and seeing how late it was, he hurriedly left.

On quitting the palace, I saw the Minister outside in conversation with General Ignatiev, the Russian Ambassador. Hussein Avni was very calm, and, I saw, refused to speak French.

The Ambassador was talking much and excitedly, and I could not help thinking of what I once heard old Mehmet Ruchtu Pasha say: "For each step the Russian takes, he tells ten lies."

CHAPTER IX

ON the first Friday of every month I paid a visit to the ladies of the household of the Prince; for though one lived in the same palace they were very ceremonious about certain customs. I began the day with the chief lady, whose position is one of considerable importance. I found her sitting on the highest of her divans with a beautiful cashmere wound round her waist, and on her head was white muslin, exquisitely painted with flowers and wreathed with other artificial flowers. This manner of doing the hair is a very pretty one, and is always called *hotoz*, the muslin and flowers being fastened with great jewelled pins, and is only worn by ladies of a certain age. From each ear hung a large pear-shaped emerald, joined by a silken thread which hung loosely on the neck.

The room with its fine gilt matting had as furniture three little divans, and at one end, in the full daylight an Egyptian bed, a perfect blaze of colour and embroidered cushions draped in mosquito curtains of pale blue Brussels net with silver woven through it.

After the usual exchange of compliments, there was silence for some time—the silence which always exists between ladies of high rank who are in no hurry to talk, but who find considerable pleasure in each other's company. As I was leaving, three ladies entered dressed in the French manner, but bowing in the graceful Turkish way. It seemed that that was the only national thing they were allowed to keep in their lives that were sacrificed to the wish to appear "*à la Franka.*"

Yellow dyed hair, tight stays, Louis XV. heels, reddened lips, frizzed hair on their foreheads—all details which they took so much trouble about, and transformed these women into merely ridiculous dolls.

If only each country could keep its national costumes, instead of copying those of their neighbours!

All the visits I paid were alike—everywhere I was welcomed with the same gentle amiability and dignity which is invariable amongst Turkish women. No unpleasant allusion was ever made to my rather peculiar position, and discretion is rigidly observed by the ladies of a harem, who carefully conceal, as if it were a dishonour, any slight disagreeable thing that might by chance spring up amongst them.

Everywhere the same simplicity, the divans of a dazzling whiteness, and all colour and air of luxury concentrated solely on the bed, with its mattresses of white watered silk, its damask coverings embroidered with golden flowers, little cushions worked in delicate designs in seed-pearls, and mosquito curtains of golden or coloured net.

I found the room of Kuchuk Oumil Bey (the prettiest and most charming of the young mothers) empty. I often went to see this attractive young woman, and greatly admired the elegance of her apartments— always fragrant with freshly-cut flowers and a soft warm air which gave the place a certain feeling of comfort and well-being. Thinking perhaps that Oumil Bey was taking her bath, I opened the door of the *hammam* where I heard the running water. On one of the divans all the young woman's garments were spread out, sparkling with gold embroideries; two hand-glasses, powder-boxes, large flacons of toilet waters; and on the ground, laid out on a large square of mauve silk, was a dressing-gown of pale soft silk, trimmed with a mass of Valenciennes lace. There was a little clatter of heels on the pavement, and Oumil Bey came in, enveloped in towels, and a white turban round her head.

After a few compliments and civilities had been exchanged, she gave herself up to her toilet, and wrapped chastely in her towels stretched out her limbs which were carefully rubbed with some sweet, milky lotion. That finished, she disappeared for a moment and returned enveloped in a cloud of soft muslin—giving one the idea of a young plant, supple and strong, that had lately been watered, and was spreading its leaves and flowers to the warm summer's sun.

.　　.　　.　　.　　.　　.　　.

I continued my round of visits, and lifting a portière I entered the apartment of Beuyuk Ouma Hanem, who was one of the favourites, for she already had two children.

She was a woman with a passionate nature, fanatical and almost violent in her desires. Her beauty, though of rather a nard type, was still remarkable, and she was possessed of masses of copper-coloured hair, with marvellously long and thickly painted eyelashes and a colourless creamy complexion. She put down her cigarette for a moment to welcome me, and then let her eyes wander vaguely and dreamily on the Bosphorus that lay stretched out at our feet.

"My spirit is slowly dying," she said softly; "nothing will ever kindle in it again the real feeling of happiness."

"But our exile will cease soon," I said gently."

"Soon—soon," she replied, lifting herself languidly on her cushions "It is with that word that we send children to sleep—and you know well our Prince is not of the race of Christian Princes to turn towards Paris like the sunflowers do to the sun ; and Paris —the famous Paris—why do they think so much of it ? I remember some years ago a son of the king called Plonplon, came to

see us at Choubra. He treated his wife
as we treat our negresses; and then another came — by name Chambord. He
ought to have been of the Islamite race,
he was so grave. Then the beautiful
Empress Eugénie, who, to recompense the
officers attached to her person, gave them
her photograph only, with her signature on
it. Not a single diamond—nothing! Aman,
it was pitiable. When sovereigns travel,"
continued Ouma Hanem with warmth, "they
ought to leave the people overcome with
admiration for their generosity, and not
only photographs behind them like celebrated wrestlers. First of all, European
sovereigns never take themselves seriously.
and then they are astonished that their
people do not respect them."

She grew animated and happy to find
a listener attentive and serious. "Here
even," she continued, "in this palace where
we are settled, and which the Khedive
offered to our Prince, we can remember one

fine example—that of the Princess Nazley. She at least was magnificent in her generosity, and terrible in her anger. Whoever was wanting in respect to her paid for it with his life. She, as you know, once inhabited this palace, and was accustomed to sleep on a mattress over which slaves held up mosquito curtains. One day one of them let fall the corner that she held up on the foot of the Princess. Immediately she caused the clumsy one to be laid on the floor, and on her bare stomach burning charcoal was put, and the Princess tranquilly drank coffee that had been heated on this strange grate. One day the husband of the Princess admired the beautiful hair of a slave who held the basin in which he washed his hands. The next morning he saw the freshly-severed head hung up by its hair to the cornice of his bed when he awoke."

After a silence, with frowning eyebrows she continued.

"Don't you see, the only powerful

sovereign is the one who makes himself feared. The royal family of Egypt has known how to be cruel, like all dynasties at the beginning of their power; but it has lost its instinct of authority, and the populace has no longer any belief in the power of kings. Look at our Prince—look at the Sultan—they are mere lambs.

Our conversation ended there, and I said farewell to the favourite Ouma Hanem.

That evening, for the first time, I was on duty near the Prince; and the prospect of watching over the heir to the throne, lying on a mattress across his doorway, with the watchword that was to prevent any one whoever it might be from entering, filled me with a sort of pride. The highest personages are always guarded thus by a woman, whilst soldiers and other guardians watch by the door of the harem.

In the interior of a harem the master enjoys absolute power. The police can never enter, and the most terrible dramas

D

might be acted there, and no one would have the right to interfere. Now, I believe life passes in them quite tranquilly, and apart from the death of Abdul Aziz I have heard of no tragedies.

Wrapped in my long night-clothes I was stretched out on my bed across the door. About eleven o'clock, after the two dressers. had gone out, I heard the Prince clap his hands. I jumped up and went in. Halim, dressed in a correct English indoors suit with his fez pushed back, was reading some European review. On recognizing me, he gave a gesture of astonishment, and getting up pushed me gently towards the door saying, "How is it that you are here so late?"

"It is my right," I answered. "I am on duty for the night, and I begin my first evening of guard."

"No, no, my child," he said, "you are not of our religion, and I should do wrong to let you be treated as if you were so."

A quick feeling of anger seized me, and I answered sharply, with rather a broken voice. "I will stay, I will stay; it would be a disgrace for me to be sent back. What reputation should I have if you should send me away from you this evening? Every one would be against me, and my life would be intolerable. I should not have the courage to live."

The Prince lit a cigar without answering me; then he opened widely the window, standing up with his back to me, and looked out on the Bosphorus which lay like a vast sheet of satin under the silver rays of the moon. The silence which followed seemed full of a great sadness, and when the Prince spoke again, his voice made me tremble vaguely.

"When you are twenty-one you shall see and choose for yourself, my child; till that moment I do not wish you to adopt Islamite customs, and if you do not give me any grave reason for displeasure, you have my word that I shall marry you. But for the moment I wish you to be odalisque only in name; I wish you to be free to choose the sort of life which seems best to you, and," he added with a smile, "perhaps you will marry a king and not a prince." Holding out his hand to me he said gently: "Stay and do your service, and keep our secret with the fidelity with which you brought the letters from the Minister of War."

"And I," I cried passionately—"I have loved you from the day I threw myself into the water to join you; when I suddenly hear your voice my heart swells as if it would choke me; if your hand touches me, it makes my blood rush through my veins, and seems to burn my skin. Your eldest daughter, who guessed my secret, when she heard you coming, used to cover my eyes with her hand, to calm the suffering in my child's heart; but I never was a child; I was tortured with jealousy; you knew it then—you know it now. I used to put my face near yours only that I might breathe your breath, and I felt my pupils dilate when I looked into your eyes; my very flesh throbbed with love if you touched my lips with yours."

My breath came in short gasps, and I could not help closing my eyes, seized as I was with a fierce longing to cry. But I had learnt to restrain all tears, so as not to displease him, though I felt that inside my heart was crying passionately, sadly.

He could no longer resist the wish to have me near him, and with a look of deepest affection he drew me to him almost roughly and kissed me on the lips.

"I love you, Ela," he said, "I love you better than desire itself, and in a way I have never yet been capable of loving. I have always lived the life of a positivist, but holding you in my arms I have discovered that I have a spirit of sentiment. I believe in a better instinct which tells

me not to take advantage of your inex-
perience. You will go to the European
life for a time, if it seems good to you,
and you shall make your choice when you
are of age. I have never believed in an
ideal love, but in this furtive moment I
believe, and I thank you for having given
me belief."

Then I put my arms close round his
neck, and swore that nothing should make
me renounce his religion, and said : "You
know I do not like European life. I
have seen, thanks to you, the luxurious
and comfortable life in great French families. Never could I accustom myself
to that life of excitement without end.
Nothing, my Prince, can take the place
of the happy harem life."

After my eight nights of guard, I went
back to my ordinary mode of life.

CHAPTER X

ONE Friday I was told to accompany the great Princess Zeinep, the eldest sister of the Prince, to the palace of the Sultana Fatma.

The Princess Zeinep had kept her immense fortune; she observed with great strictness the Mussulman traditions. Intelligent, proud, and very pious, she rarely even received ambassadresses. Nevertheless, Madame de Gasparin was received by her, and kept always a delightful memory of that interview. The Princess was devoted to her brother Halim, which she proved by leaving him all her fortune. She lived in the greatest magnificence in the palace of Bebek, and rarely visited the Sultanas. These visits were a great

expense on account of the money and
jewels which was the custom to distribute
amongst the wives of the Sultan.

Notwithstanding that she never allowed
a French dress in her harem, she sent an
order that I was to be dressed in the latest
Parisian fashion. She thought that thus
I should be more easily noticed by the
Sultana, to whom she wished to present
me. The Prince was interested in this,
and sent me from his treasury a pair of
earrings which were said to have belonged
to Marie Antoinette. They were single
diamonds cut in the shape of almonds, and
he begged that I would wear no other
jewels.

The Sultana Fatma lived like an idol in
the depths of her palace. Daughter of
Abdul Medjed, it was she who, after the
Crimean War, used to drive about in
a carriage with massive silver wheels,
shaded by a large umbrella with a diamond
fringe, the handle of which was ornamented

with an enormous ruby the size of a pigeon's egg, which gave the French ambassador, Monsieur Thouvenel, many sad reflections. Up to the death of her father, she lived as a celebrity in all Oriental annals; and the people listened with open ears and eyes to the marvellous descriptions of her luxury and magnificence.

For many long years the Sultana Fatma had lived a retired life in the palace of Balta Liman, where I entered behind the Princess Zeinep. On going in we heard first of all in the distance the professional laughers, and nothing was more peculiar than the sound of that unreal mirth, which echoed in the silence like a pebble dropped in a well.

Laid out in those vast and deserted rooms were the presents made to Abdul Medjed by foreign sovereigns, Louis XVI. candelabras, gilt furniture, stately old Sèvres china, great vases from Japan and China unknown in any trade. On cabinets, in every style, were antique clocks ranged symmetrically, and in place of honour you saw stuffed birds on musical boxes which played Parisian airs. Gold vases, silver boxes encrusted with stones, stuffs embroidered with pearls, a thousand precious things which remained there till the Sultana, pressed for money, allowed some Jew dealer to carry off a load of them.

After a wait of an hour the Princess and I were admitted into the presence of the Sultana Fatma. She was very particular that all the ceremonial of genuflexion should be rigorously carried out; and it was only after all the customary salutations were made that I dared lift my eyes to her, when for the first time I saw a Sultana.

She was a woman with a face as absolutely immovable and expressionless as that of a goddess. Her eyes, which nothing could astonish or interest, gazed into vacancy with a look of complete authority, so absolute that they made one uncomfortable.

Clothed in a dress of a strange green colour, with not even a jewel to break the uniformity, she preserved a silence that was only broken by the professional laughers. Slowly she asked after the health of the Princess, who answered her without omitting a single word of the compliments and formulas that were necessary. She wished to see me clearly, and made me go close to her, examining me curiously, like a bit of carved ivory is inspected by connoisseurs. At a sign, a lady of the palace appeared dressed in white satin, with golden dyed hair, in which were birds of paradise made of large pearls.

" Ela Hanem will dine with us," said the Sultana in an expressionless voice—such a voice as the dead Caliphs must use when they talk together in their vast burial place.

The dinner was remarkable ; the slaves in low cut ball-dresses carried the immense dishes, which were of rare china, gold or silver ; the table sparkled with a fairylike brilliancy. The attendants walked slowly, or held themselves immovable with their arms crossed and the head thrown a little backwards, and their white throats thrust out. The Sultana could keep a sort of illusion to herself of great wealth when she saw all this luxury about her ; but away from there, in the depths of the palace, the slaves of the fourth rank were most uncomfortable, and complained bitterly of their distress.

On leaving the palace, the lady in waiting of the Princess distributed the customary presents amongst the immediate entourage of the Sultana, and that simple visit cost the Princess four hundred pounds. And it struck me that it would be pleasanter to watch the waters of the Bosphorus than to go often and kiss the stuff on the divan of a Sultana—a praiseworthy sentiment of independence, doubtless instilled into me by the European reviews which the Prince had lent me to read. That evening on going in

I watched for some time the sunset with its blaze of gold and rose-coloured clouds, and I listened to the Muezzin who chanted his prayer to Allah. It was a hymn of infinite sadness which left one's heart bruised with a mysterious pain. I hid my face in my hands, moved with a great pity for all sufferings of which I knew nothing, and the voice of that man made me guess at.

CHAPTER XI

THREE days later we left for Brousse, where the Princess Zeinep went to drink the waters, and the Prince, her brother, to hunt bears.

This journey necessitated an entire re-arranging of things, and it was necessary to hire a ship to carry the suite and slaves. The governor of Brousse gave a fête to welcome worthily their Highnesses, and the peasants of Mount Olympus came down into the plain to see this unusual spectacle.

There was an old and blind saint there who had the gift of prophecy; for living entirely for God he had second sight, and those who were fortunate enough to kiss his hand felt a wonderful peace enter their hearts. Nothing could surpass the whiteness of his fine cashmere *caftans*, and his high cap was wound round with muslin that no human hand had ever touched. It was said that two angels wound and unwound the turban of the old saint during his sleep, and this charming belief brought happiness to sad hearts—at least so they said.

Soon after her arrival the Princess, sitting on her cushions and surrounded by her attendants, received him with much civility, offering him a chibouk and coffee, and listened with deference when he expressed his regret that the young Mussulmen of the country were so prone to forsake the ancient customs in favour of the new Paris fashions. The saint was right, for the Ottomans had everything to lose by doing so, and nothing to gain in giving up the sacred principles of the Koran. And the young women imitating the faults, without acquiring the virtues, might do well to think seriously about the change.

From the moment of his reaching Brousse, the Prince gave himself up entirely to bear-hunting, and a pleasure that only rich people can indulge in. A hundred peasants with flaming resinous torches drove the animal towards the Prince and his mamelukes, and part of the night was always spent in this amusement. On one occasion he killed one of the finest animals I had ever seen—a female bear followed by two of her cubs; the latter were captured alive.

These same little animals, three months later, entered the hall where lay stretched out the skins of the bears that had been killed, and where amongst all the others they recognised that of their mother, and howled dismally over it. They had the greatest difficulty in leading the poor animals away.

Sometimes they used to claw at the negresses' hair, and ended by creating a great terror in the minds of the black

hood, and became pashas, and grand viziers during the reign of the Sultan.

I also paid a visit to the excellent Mahmoud Damate Pasha, who had married the Sultana Djemilee. I found him as usual smoking his pipe in the garden. It is the custom that, when a man has been honoured by a Sultana for a wife, one can only enter a harem with elaborate ceremonies, and be admitted after a distinct invitation, and can only sit at a distance from the wife, on a stool, with no friendly familiarity unless it comes from the lady herself.

Thus many Sultanas keep their husbands waiting for an hour or so at their doors, and the wretched man is so closely watched that he loses any sense of liberty of action.

For this reason young men have a holy horror of being chosen as husbands for the princesses of the blood. Formerly if the man refused the marriage, he often died of a sudden and strange malady; but it seems that in these later times the microbe of that illness has disappeared.

Mahmoud Eamate, having succeeded in making his wife love him, was not unhappy, and one day proposed that he should present me to his wife, and the ceremonial was slightly shortened.

He paused at the entrance to her apartment, awaiting a feeble sign to present me, and then placed himself on a stool at a respectful distance. Djemile Sultana had certainly rather a grand appearance notwithstanding that she suffered from inflammation of the eye-lids, which forced her to keep her eyes nearly closed. She was dressed quite simply in Indian mauve muslin, and made me sit close to her on the divan so that she could see me the more clearly—then, pinching my cheek, she said, " It is well, you may retire," which I did walking backwards, as is the custom. The reception struck me as being rather cold, but at the moment I passed with the

Pasha from the harem into the courtyard, we met a eunuch who presented me with a gold cage in which was a stuffed bird with ruby eyes and which warbled a Parisian tune.

Mahmoud Pasha seemed delighted with this attention from his august wife, and assured me that I had made a conquest. So I left, holding in one hand my train, and in the other the gilded cage.

I was present at the fêtes given in honour of the sister of R—— Bey on the occasion of her marriage. He had formerly been Turkish ambassador to Paris under Napoleon III.

All the great Ottoman families were asked to this wedding, which was celebrated according to all the ancient traditions. The bride looked lovely under her veil of gold thread, with tiny flowers in diamonds fastened on her forehead, cheeks, and chin, and passed through the harem on the arm of her husband. He kept his eyes on the ground, so as not to see the women, to whom he threw handfuls of small silver pieces, which were eagerly picked up, for they are supposed to bring good luck.

The husband thus leads his wife to the room she will occupy in the harem, and places her on a divan, where she stays throughout the whole day, covered with jewels, and absolutely silent, not speaking to any one, even if they should speak to her. The husband then retires, and in the evening after the festivities he re-enters the room where he has left her, and lifts her veil, seeing the face of his wife for the first time.

Grand Ottoman marriages last three days, and are made the occasions of magnificent fêtes. Of late years they have lost much of their *éclat*

The one I was present at was graced with the presence of two titled ladies from the palace of Adile Sultana, and of Taïfur Aga, a eunuch of very high rank, who was constantly with His Majesty the Sultan.

Taïfur Aga was an extremely handsome Abyssinian, fair, and with a bright colour, fine eyes, with slightly waving hair and dazzling teeth, a straight nose with sensitive nostrils like a hunted gazelle. His natural air of distinction, calm manners, his sweet and rather sad look gave him a great charm.

His hands and feet betokened race, and he was always dressed by Poole with perfect taste, and never wore any jewels. His voice even was delightful, unlike that of most eunuchs, and it was always whispered that he was in love with a French actress of the theatre at Pera.

He asked to be presented to me, and paid me many compliments on my appearance, and talked for so long a time to me as to cause some jealousy amongst the ladies of the harem; for he was much sought after by those who were ambitious for imperial favour. In the evening I recounted the incident to Prince Halim, who seemed very pleased, and said to me, "If he pays you a visit, do all you can to please him," adding with a sigh, "Through him perhaps I shall be able one day to return to Egypt!"

The next day Taïfur Aga and the second chief eunuch were announced at the harem, where they were received with all the honours of their high rank. They asked to be allowed to see the Prince, who received them standing up, a form of etiquette reserved only for the Grand Vizier. This mark of courtesy was not wasted; for by this the Prince obtained the opportunities of communicating directly with His Majesty the Sultan without having to make use of ministers as intermediates. How could one tell whether this *rapprochement* might not be the means of giving him his throne?

CHAPTER XIII

SHORTLY after this visit I was again entrusted to carry a heavy bag to the Minister of War, and I knew it contained money.

The Minister, when I arrived, hardly looked at me, for he was busy signing papers at his desk. Everything was changed in his surroundings. The *aides-de-camp* were there in crowds, ambassadors asked to be received, ministers waited in the adjoining rooms seeking audience.

Hussein Avni lived in a perpetual fever, a centre of gold-covered uniforms, whose wearers brought him messages from the Sultan—or his coffee.

Everything was done in silence and every face was expressionless, each one trying to exaggerate his own importance.

General Ignatiev, the Russian ambassador, had the cunning look of an old fox. Monsieur de Vogüé the French ambassador, calm, distinguished and inoffensive. Sir H. Elliot of England, rather washed out, but extremely *correct*.

Hussein Avni looked aged, and his beard had grown grey, but his eyes were full of fire in his rather full face, having that look of vigour which marks the Kurd, whilst his teeth were those of a man who had always devoured roasted meat in the open air. When he saw me, he held out his hand, and I felt a tightening at my heart, for I felt that something of grave importance must have taken place. I kissed his hand, whilst he said in a gentle voice with a certain intimacy in it : "Carry the bag to my room, listen to all the complaints of my wife, and send word that you will not return home to-night, for I shall have several things to say to you when I am in the harem."

He came in about eight o'clock tired out,
and had a cold bath to refresh him. Sitting
on his divan, in a long fur-lined garment.
he rested with his hands over his eyes.
A slave came in saying : " Pasha Effendi,
the Sultan asks for you."

Quickly he got into his uniform and went
out murmuring : " I can no longer do it ;
it is at an end."

His eyes were hard, and his wife complained that doubtless it was glorious to
be always necessary to one's sovereign,
but that the Pasha was tired out, adding :
"God grant a long life to our Sultan !
we are only his humble servants."

I did not see him again till five in the
morning, and his first words were : "Everything is arranged ; the Sultan wishes to see
you—Taïfur Aga has spoken about you ;
you must go at once, for they will come
to fetch you from the Prince's palace."

I felt as if a heavy weight had fallen
on my heart, and I thought I was going

to faint. The Sultan wished to see me! I was to be presented to the Turkish Emperor, and perhaps should be obliged to leave my beloved Prince!

The Pasha smoked his chibouk silently; then, like a man who can at last speak openly without being overheard, said : " He really amuses me, that Russian Ignatiev. He proposed making a revolution in the palace that would dethrone the Sultan for the good of the empire. He thinks that nothing can be done without him, and he wishes to be extremely clever. It is the surest way of being taken in. I told him that the thing was impossible, but I thanked him very much, and now he is quite satisfied, and feels quite certain that he knows what is going to be done. Ah! he is very amusing."

Then he began to laugh quietly, a laugh that was almost soundless.

"May the curses of heaven fall on the Russian who wishes to touch our sovereign."

cried the wife of the minister in her loud voice, "and may his live entrails be torn to pieces by the dogs in the streets."

Hussein Pasha then proposed to his wife, in a tone of voice that would brook no denial, that she should go and see if their son's turban was in its place, and when we were alone, he put his short hand with its strong square fingers on my head, saying :

"Your fidelity to your master is worthy of ancient legends. We are sure of you, my child, and we shall want your help."

This preamble made a little shiver run through me, and I listened with all my ears as the Pasha continued :

"The money that you brought me has had the effect of quieting the scruples of some tiresome people. In three months the revolution will have taken place and the Sultan dethroned. For two years I have worked without ceasing, and Allah knows with what energy. The end happily is in sight. If you knew what a terrible task this has been, to prepare the minds of the ministers for the change of sovereigns. It was necessary to gain Cheik ul Islam over to the conspiracy, and to obtain the support of all the Softas.

Europe will never know that this revolution has been carried out by will of a single patriot. I don't know whether any personal ambition is mixed up in this desire to save the empire ; if it were, it would be inconsistent in me. For the moment my end is only to save the country from imminent ruin. If the Sultan would only curb his mad expenditure, this revolution would never have entered my mind. It is only in the face of his disdain of reforms for the existence of his empire, that quite suddenly one night when I could not sleep I knew it was necessary to dethrone him. I am still astonished that I should have thought such a thing so absolutely at variance with our customs and ideas. How strange it is ! It can only be from having read so much foreign literature, which un-consciously has impregnated my mind."

After a short silence he went on :

"Your Prince, who waits always to regain his throne of Egypt, has every-thing to gain by this revolution. Mourad Effiendi, whom we mean to place on the throne, will give it him by *irade*, annulling that of the present Sultan by changing the succession. In a few days I shall no longer be Grand Vizier, for I shall only keep my position as Minister of War. When the moment comes, so as to avoid all suspicion, I shall leave for Brousse, and my return will be the signal for the *coup d'état*. Before all things, I wish the dethroned Sultan to be treated with all the respect that is his due. I do not wish a hair of his head to be touched, for were it necessary that his life should be taken, we would sooner re-nounce all idea of crowning Mourad Effindi. He has only agreed to accept the throne on condition that his uncle is treated with all

gentleness and respect. Everything is arranged with the ministers, and you can help
us to dethrone Abdul Aziz without bloodshed
or violence—and it is Allah who has inspired
His Majesty with a wish to have you near
him. We are convinced that we shall have
no bloody deeds with which to reproach
ourselves, unless at the last moment circum-
stances go against us. Listen to me with
all your attention, and remember well what
I am going to tell you, for the time has come
when you will see me rarely."

"Don't count on me," I answered in a
dull, heavy voice that I hardly recognised
as mine. "I will never play this infamous
rôle of smiling in his face, the better to spy
on him, and give him up defenceless to a
conspiracy that shatters his reign. If I go
to him, I will serve him faithfully, but not
as a traitor. And if I am to be the means
of obtaining the throne of Egypt for my
master — for the man I love—it will be
honestly, and not by a monstrous act. No,

no, I refuse—I refuse it even to my Prince.
God knows whether we should ever get the
throne. Our life has no other end, no other
hope, it is true, and exile is a bitter fruit—
the only one we have the right to touch;
but it is better to taste that bitterness, even
to death, than to become traitors who hit a
defenceless man."

"Machallah," Hussein Avni interrupted,
"you talk idly and stupidly. You speak of
selling, of buying, of betraying. I tell you
simply that I shall be happier if you are near
the Sultan; you will certainly save his life,
and it is for that that I wish you to obtain
his entire confidence, and you will have it,
for it is written, and everything arranges
itself with the help of God even. It is
necessary that I shall be able to enter the
harem of the palace, to conduct Mourad
from there and lead him to the War Office,
where, before all the united ministers, he
will be acknowledged as sovereign, and will
sign the *irade* dethroning Abdul Aziz. It

E

is only thus that Abdul can be deposed, and you understand the gravity of the situation. If Abdul defends himself and sees Mourad, I shall be obliged to send my sword through him.   Otherwise we should all be hung— your Prince also; it would be a general massacre. Everything must happen without noise, without tragedy—your entry into the palace facilitates things very much.   I wish to save my country, but not to stain my hands in blood.   Fortunately the foreign Powers have no idea of what is about to be done—no false slip has been made.   Everything is thought out and matured.   That old fox Ignatiev is so well humbugged that he will be ill from it, and all the ambassadors will be taken by surprise.   They will know nothing of the *coup d'état* till the hundred and one guns announce it to all Europe. Will you—yes, or no—have the throne of Egypt for your master, and prevent him from being sprinkled with the blood of Abdul Aziz? If yes, you have but to take service

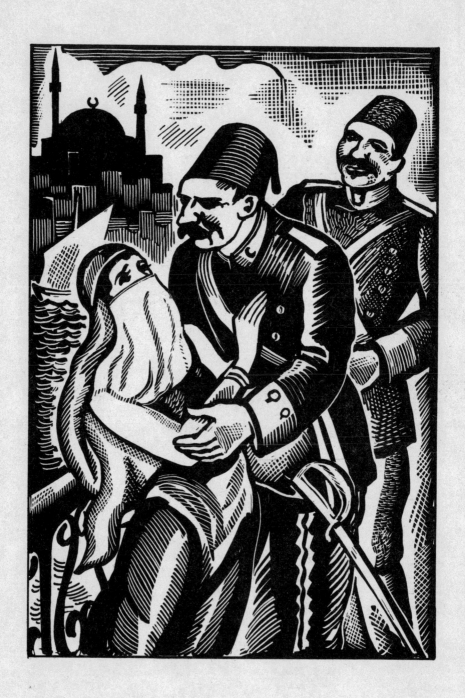

with His Majesty, and in proper time and place I will explain what you will have to do. Of one thing be sure : Whether you say yes or no, your refusal will not stop a revolution like this one ; it may only render it a tragedy —that is all. If I put it before you from a motive of sentiment, it is because my human feelings are touched, but—I should know my duty as a soldier, if it were necessary."

" Have you thougnt of your daughter Hairiee ? " I asked, with a voice that had lost all expression. He reddened slightly and said :

" Hairiee wants for nothing ; my fortune is made ; you must have noticed that we no longer live our former life ; besides, she is about to be married, and in this she has nothing to gain—and I—I think only of the good of my country."

" And yet you are the only man the Sultan trusts."

" Yes—but there are days when he is suspicious ; I am never sure of the morrow."

"That is it — with the Sultan one never knows. Is he really mad as they say?"

"No, not exactly, but peculiar—capricious. It is extravagance, the ill-balanced mind of an autocrat, who does not know whether he wishes a thing or not. It is impossible to do anything with him, there is nothing left but to depose him. The chief eunuch is one of us, without whom it is impossible to act, and he gives us his weight in exchange for a large fortune. He has undertaken that once the deposition is signed by Sultan Mourad, that he will break the news to the deposed Sultan, and tell him, that he must immediately leave the palace, and go to the Vieux Sérail. We were doubtful where to find an ally in the harem, and now, by the desire of the Sultan himself, everything is as we wished. And I thank Allah for it, whilst confiding to you—a woman— the secrets of the conspiracy. I see that you will never speak, for your Prince would be one of the first to be hung on Acq Meidan; go, and God guide your steps!"

Very much upset as I was, I had the strength to get up, and bowing to the Pasha, I felt that my cheeks were wet with tears, whilst, almost unconsciously, I said as I withdrew: "The pity of it— oh! the pity of it. No good will come to us through it all."

CHAPTER XIV

THE hour was come to say good-bye to the Prince.

"Never," he cried, "will I consent to any attempt on the life of the Sultan. I would sooner give the whole thing up, and if matters are not carried out as we settled, I shall retire, and shall give no more money. Now, you are *au courant*, and I am glad to be able to talk to you about it. You must know that I have done all in my power to have annulled the *irade* that changed the succession to the throne of Egypt in favour of Ismaël. But the Sultan was immovable and would not hear of it. I shall not mix myself up in this *coup d'état*, which I dislike. I give only my money, and not my advice, and that only for obtaining from Mourad,

in the event of his reigning, the possession
of my throne of Egypt. Ah! how I wish I
could reach that end by some other means—
if only the influence of Taïfur could accomplish it."

Despite the passionate kisses with which
he covered my lips, I felt instinctively that
the Prince's whole soul was absorbed in
the affair, and as I left him I could only
think sadly of the words of an old woman of
the harem : "Ah!" she said, "it is a doubtful
happiness loving a grand seigneur."

. . . .

When Taïfur Aga came to fetch me, he
asked to be received by the Prince, and
in my presence he assured him that I should
be as free in the Sultan's palace as in that of
the Prince.

"We know," he said, "that she is Islamite
at heart, but not yet by act, and if it pleases
her to go out unveiled, she is at liberty to
do so. If the Sultan wishes to have Ela
Hanem at the palace, it is that he is bored,

and he is curious to see her, having heard her much talked about by several of his ministers. His favourite chamberlain, Nevrez Pasha, has told him much that interested him of the childhood of Ela Hanem. For some time our sovereign has been a prey to melancholy; all that she can do to amuse him will be blest by Allah. She shall do just as she pleases, and when she wishes to go out, a carriage or a *caïq* will be at her orders.

CHAPTER XV

NEVER shall I forget what I felt when, preceded by Taïfur Aga, I entered the harem of the Sultan and went through that superb-looking crowd of magnificent women, who are suspicious of all things outside, and walk with their heads held high as if they regulated the destiny of the world, though they have no other care than to arrange the ceremonials of their rank and settle the questions of precedence. They separated to make way for Taifur Aga, and sat down at some distance, with haughty looks and proud attitudes. A chill fell on my heart, my limbs grew heavy and my head dizzy as I advanced. A great charm and look of high-breeding made most of these women extremely attractive.

Some of them looked at me with the appearance of indifference—after all, one more woman in a crowd of about two thousand is not a thing of great importance. They showed the greatest civility to Taïfur, as he was a person with whom it was necessary to be on good terms. They formed pretty groups, and their clothes, all of tender and delicate shades, made a harmonious whole, like a garden of beautiful flowers. Ripples and occasional bursts of laughter floated through those immense rooms, and I was astonished at only seeing fair women as I passed along.

Always a little superstitious, I said to myself that if I did not see one dark one before I reached the room prepared for me, it would be a bad omen. As if the happiness of my life depended on it, I looked right and left, hoping to see one with dark eyes and hair.

Not one could I see, and a sort of despair seized me, for I felt that if I wished to fly, I should never find the means for deliverance.

. . . .

Eight days passed, whilst I waited to be summoned to the presence of the "*Effendimez*"—as the Sultan is called by the people of the court—and unconsciously I copied the manners and haughty bearing of the ladies in waiting on the Sultan. I was at once taken up by a group of these *grandes dames*, who showered presents and civilities on me.

We used to walk in a large garden surrounded by walls so high that they tired one to think of what was passing outside amongst the beings who were only simple subjects. All the mad desires, wishes and caprices of spoilt children were realized there, and after a day or two I hardly noticed them. Every word spoken was refined, everything was graceful and light, and the Parisian influence of taste was sufficiently felt everywhere to make things perfect. There the women never felt that life could be sad. They laughed, recited verses, gave fêtes amongst each other, and drove out to look for new things to buy, coming home accompanied by slaves and eunuchs laden with their purchases. If marriages took place, they served as excuses for the buying of beautiful things, for promenades, for pleasure parties, and feasts of sugared and sweet things. Amongst all this somewhat wild luxury nothing the least improper was ever allowed, and the advice and wishes of the Mistresses of Ceremonies were always carefully obeyed.

"Ladies," they used to say, "be careful that your bearing when you are together is always full of grace, modesty, and nobility, and never forget that the King whom you serve is the chosen of Allah."

The morals of the *sérail* still kept a certain old-fashioned simpleness in spite of all the splendour. The most grave discussions were often held on so trivial a subject as to whether Melek or Hatije would marry a man with a beard or only a moustache. The little slaves in side-rooms learnt their lessons in music and dancing from Turkish and Armenian professors, under the watchful eye of a eunuch.

When evening was come and, as with the Prince of Egypt, the muezzin had sung "*Allah u Eckber*," there began the pompous entry of the attendants in their magnificent embroidered clothes, bearing on their heads the immense covered dishes draped with purple silk.

As this magnificent procession went by, I could not help thinking of my childhood and my happy hours in the harem of the Prince. My thoughts carried me even further back, and I saw in fancy the gentle, honest Doudou to whom I used to say, "I will be *séraile*," when we used to gossip in front of her cottage by the sea. And now I had reached that dignity, and large tears fell from my eyes—not unhappy ones, but healthy and natural, like the drops of a summer storm.

Ah! Vai Yarabi! how my heart sank!

A great silence suddenly fell on the palace, and I heard a sound like the fluttering of wings of a bird that beat against the windows of a mosque. I looked round me with surprise—for it was a wild and general flight of all the women, who flitted noiselessly away, holding their very breath, frightened at the approach of some great power.

Certainly the first instinct ought to be one of flight from the fear of being seen by the master. They hid themselves wildly behind the marble columns; and I, transfixed with curiosity, stood still at the entrance to my room, in front of the hanging golden *portière*, against which I must have stood in high relief like a Russian saint. My yellow hair framed my face like a halo of light and my eyes were wide open. I understood too late to hide myself.

The Sultan and Validé, his mother, came near me, and I stood motionless as a statue. They passed, and my eyes brightened with emotion, whilst my hand grasped the *portière* to support my trembling body. That evening I was summoned to appear before His Majesty.

It was my duty to serve the evening meal, and a Mistress of the Ceremonies taught me the necessary customs to be observed in the presence of His Majesty. I was to hold myself erect, with head up and arms crossed, and to answer clearly and briefly any questions, and to use the title of *Effendimez* in addressing the Sultan. Everything was to be done with almost military precision. When, conducted by Taïfur Aga, I entered the Imperial apartment, my heart failed me. I was seized with a vague fear, and crossed my arms on my breast.

Sitting on a low divan covered with purple silk embroidered in pale gold, the Sultan was looking out on the Bosphorus. I thought he was contemplating me, but I dared not lift my eyes to his face. The silence was so profound that I heard my own heart beating. "He also will hear it, and will send me away!" I said to myself.

Some time passed before he took any notice of me or made any movement. I slowly lifted my eyes and saw the King of Kings. Out of kindness he pretended not to know that I looked at him, and occupied himself with a book that lay on a cushion near him. Again I ventured to look, and I saw more clearly. He struck me as handsome, and as having a decidedly majestic appearance. A fine head, broad shoulders, and his bare neck was that of a wrestling giant.

He was clothed in several long garments of fine white cloth, and his arms being bare to the elbows, I saw that the skin was white, strong, and healthy. Thrown loosely round his shoulders was a black cloak lined with beautiful sables, of such a quality that could never be bought through the traders, and that must have cost at least four thousand pounds ; his bare feet were thrust into red morocco slippers, and on his head a scarlet fez bound with the finest of white cambric.

He used to change his fez three or four times a day. A manufactory of these articles was established near the palace for his use alone.

"Do war-ships interest you?" he asked, still with his eyes fixed on the Bosphorus. His voice sounded so kindly, and I saw there was even more of a smile in his eyes than on his lips, that, quite forgetting the etiquette, I made a step towards him, blushed furiously, and completely lost my *sang-froid.* Monsieur de Vogüé is right, I thought quickly ; he is a great Emperor and impresses one, and I remembered the words of the French ambassador : "I have seen all the sovereigns of Europe : not one of them has the majesty and dignity of Sultan Abdul Aziz."

He signed to me to come near, and a strange sympathy drew me to him in spite of my fear, and I tried to look right into his eyes so that I might read his soul, feeling sure that I should not displease him.

" If you desire anything," he said gently, " I am prepared to grant it to you."

" I desire nothing, your Majesty, except to serve you in the way that pleases you best."

" You are not like the rest—I can never grant them enough ; they do not dare say so, but I know it." He turned again towards the Bosphorus, sighing, and begun, half under his breath, reciting to himself some poetry that I listened to tremblingly.

I felt that my strength was going, and walking backwards, I leant for support against the delicately carved wooden columns that supported the entrance to the room.

The Sultan was very fond of solitude, and spent long hours in lonely dreamings in that room in the palace that looked out on the sea. The ladies who were on duty never showed themselves unless summoned by him by the clapping of his hands.

The vast neighbouring rooms were deserted and silent, and the eunuch on duty (who was nearly always Taïfur Aga) occupied a small chamber close by, ready to carry orders and messages from His Majesty to his chamberlains, marshals, and ministers. If the Sultan ever appeared in the court-yard, the chamberlains moved off to a respectful distance amongst the various rooms, waiting till they were called.

Half an hour passed, and I remained leaning against the column, when I heard a light step behind me, and Taïfur Aga entered.

"What is it?" asked the Sultan.

"It is the ambassadors who wish to present their letters to your Majesty. The ceremony has been put off several times, and the Grand Vizier asks whether it is your Majesty's pleasure that it should take place to-morrow?"

The Sultan started; his face contracted with anger, and frowning heavily he said in a hard dry voice: "Let them go to hell. If they like, I will receive them as I am, but nothing will induce me to put on a uniform—I won't do it."

He got up quickly and passed in front of me, and I, as if led by some irresistible force, followed him.

In a large neighbouring room was the celebrated Hussein, his Majesty's wrestler, with only a loin-cloth round him. In a moment the Sultan had torn off all his garments, and threw himself on him, without a word being spoken, and the struggle commenced. It was a serious fight, and not a simple amusement of a prince who was bored with nothing to do. I saw the Sultan bending under the embrace of the wrestler, and it made me shiver, and for a moment I was so frightened that I thought of rushing to his assistance; and almost unconsciously I drew out a long gold pin from my hair to stab the athlete, when I saw him lying on the floor half suffocated, for the Sultan had thrown him.

His Majesty then with a slow and firm step walked to the harem.

"It would be terrible," I said to myself, "if he should ever defend himself,' and I closed my eyes to shut out the vision of what might be in the future.

.   .   .   .

The Sultan pushed open a door and I followed. Though I was well accustomed to Oriental magnificence, I could not restrain a cry of admiration on entering the bath of his Majesty. There were three rooms of the purest white marble carved like the most delicate lace. In the centres were large silver fountains where scented water was running; in one corner was a basin and sprinkling cup of jade, specimens

probably unique in the world.   The white
marble couches were inlaid with silver.

When one had once seen the luxury in
which the Sultan lived, one could well understand what became of the vast sums that
he drew from the State.

He himself turned on the stream of cold
water over his head, and two slaves wrapped
him round with towels fringed with emeralds
and pearls.

Then he returned to the room where I
first found him, and sitting on the divan
he took up his telescope and gazed for a
long time at his beautiful fleet.   He was
very fond of his battleships, and Allah
spared him the pain of seeing them de-
stroyed by the torpedoes in the war of 1877.

All the boats and the public embarkations
were at a great distance from the palace,
and it was impossible to see what was going
on with the naked eye.   But the Sultan
watched everything that took place on the
Bosphorus with a telescope.

Suddenly he began to speak in a sweet grave voice without turning his head towards me.

"Ah," he said, "living before this wonderful view is the sweetest thing in my life. My journey through Europe showed me nothing so beautiful or bright. In Paris I only thought with sadness and fear that I should perhaps never see our blessed country again. Those fêtes in Europe, where the sovereigns showed themselves to the populace as if they were phenomenons, irritated me. In London I was obliged to exhibit myself when the crowd shouted in my ears. That day I actually beat poor Fuad Pasha when he insisted upon putting on my overcoat and making me appear on the bridge of my yacht. What a pitiable condition do these kings live in in Europe! What a horrible voyage! I still am nervous when I think of it.

"But with what immense delight I re-entered my empire where the sun and moon shine, as they shine nowhere else. God loves all people, but we are the heart of His chosen ones, and I am the king He loves best. When my yacht entered the Bosphorus, the trees and hills wreathed with fires lit up both shores; all the houses were illuminated. Flames of colour ran down to the edge of the sea, and far away my fleet sparkled like a bouquet of stars, and I, standing on the bridge of the boat, with my sword in my hand, looked on my people in delight. The cry they shouted—"*Padischahmez bine yacha,*" moved my very heart; it was prettier to listen to than the *hou-hou* of the English and the *vivats* of the French. With us the acclamations of the people come from their hearts. When the Empress Eugénie came, the illuminations were less beautiful, and I was sorry for it; but I had so many annoyances over that visit, that I made up my mind never to receive other sovereigns. Not one of the Sultanas would consent to see the Empress, and I was obliged to present one of the ladies of the court as Queen Mother.

"When she had gone, my mother ordered everything she had touched to be burnt. Other sovereigns have tiring habits, but I like best to be quiet. I send officers to Paris and London to learn sciences—and it seems to me that they learn many things unconnected with science."

The Sultan ceased speaking, and looked at me as if asking my opinion. I took the opportunity to tell him all the harm that I thought the European education under French and English governesses had done in the rich harems, which seemed to astonish him slightly.

"I know, I know," he went on. "I shall see to stopping the propagation of false ideas. As Turkish women cannot, and ought not to live a European life, it is illogical to bring them up on the principles of the women over there. After all, what do the young Islamites educated in the

European manner complain of, only that they cannot live the life of frail women, as in the streets of Paris. They have not even as formerly, the complaint to make about polygamy, which for some reason or other has disappeared. Who are the Pashas, Beys, or Effendis who have more than one wife? Search well, Ela Hanem, you who know all the well-conducted harems; count them; there is the Khedive, the Prince your master, old Dervich Pasha, and I. Not one of my ministers has more than one wife. A few years ago I very much wished for the wife of M—— Effendi, Three times he refused to give her to me, saying that he had married her before the *Immane*, and that in Europe they called me the Great Turk, and that I had designs on every woman. She was so beautiful, that woman, that I used to dream of her at night. Afterwards I knew that she loved one of my aides-de-camp, and that she used to admit him at night, letting down her long hair by the window to help him to climb in, whilst her husband slept. It sounds like a French fairy tale, does it not?" His Majesty added with a smile.

Going from one story to another, the Sultan told me of the amusing scruples of Monsieur de Montgascon, temporarily chargé d'affaires at the French Embassy. A Pasha whom he was visiting expressed a wish to present Madame de Montgascon to his wife in the harem. The chargé d'affaires asked the Pasha nervously: "Can I be sure that my wife will run no danger on entering Your Excellency's harem?"

"No, Monsieur," he answered. "Madame is exposed to less danger in my harem than anywhere else; and her severity of expression places her at least in a position of safety."

"They are never wanting in simplicity in the diplomatic career," continued the Sultan, smiling, "as you will see when they come to present me their credentials.

After they have gone, my chamberlains imitate them to perfection. It is about the only thing my officers can do. One of these days I will put on my uniform and we will amuse ourselves with them. Nevertheless, I have noticed amongst the ambassadors Monsieur de Vogué, who is very distinguished in his manners and very inoffensive; as to the Englishman, he knows his métier well; he is always determined to take precedence."

The familiarity with which the Sultan treated me did not astonish me much; for do not the great ones of the earth always follow their most rapid impulses? But what did astonish me was his wise and conciliatory judgment, and his matter-of-fact character. "But he is much less strong than those who wish to dethrone him," I said to myself, and I felt that my face became grave as the expression of those who watch by the dead.

The Sultan ate, sometimes in one room,

sometimes in another. He had a large appetite, and would eat in one day several dozen eggs, three chickens, etc., etc. The tray was wrapped up in a large gauze veil embroidered in gold, of which the edges were all fastened together by a ribbon on which the Empress Mother had put her seal.

He himself examined the seal, and finding it intact, he was satisfied that he ran no risk of poison ; one of the bearers then cut the seal, and the food was served.

The hour had come, and six slaves of great beauty came behind the tray and placed gold plates before the Sultan, and I tried to move off without being observed when I heard him say, " Stay, Ela Hanem."

I was faint with want of food and fatigue, but, like a woman, I felt I was beginning to love him, who made me suffer. No, not love, but only a devotion to this sovereign, who would so soon be deposed and unhappy.

By a strange coincidence, which impressed me as an evil omen, he spoke much about Napoleon III.

"How could that king live through his misfortune?" he said. "In his place, I should have killed myself—— Yes, indeed, he ought to have done it. It was not manly," he added.

That evening I went to my room worn out with fatigue, and went to bed without food, for in the palace, if once the hour for food has passed, it is impossible to get anything to eat.

CHAPTER XVI

THE Sultan Abdul Aziz was devoted to two people—his eldest son Youssouf Izzetdin, and his own mother Validé Sultana, a Circassian, and still possessed of great beauty. High-minded, proud and fanatical, she lived like a divinity. Her influence on her son was absolute. The Sultan was the most obedient son in the Empire.

Voluntarily ignorant of the change in the morals and customs of the Turkish nation, Validé Sultana continued to live after the manner of old days, surrounded by the ladies of her court as if in a fortress built of Mussulman pride. Her idea of luxury was to have everything in white or pearl-grey, and every one knows that delicate shades are the most expensive. Her slaves, exquisitely dressed, considered themselves vastly superior to the wives of the ministers; and when the Empress of the French was received by the Sultan, not one of them would condescend to carry her a cup of coffee. In spite of myself, in those surroundings I too assumed rather haughty airs; but this pride, which was so strong a feeling in the palace, had nothing aggressive or disagreeable in it, and only gave to those who felt it a certain dignity —almost a beauty.

.   .   .   .   .

One morning, whilst I was having my shoulders and neck rubbed by a slave, a messenger entered hurriedly and said, "Quickly, Ela Hanem, Validé Sultana is asking for you."

Rather nervously I got up, rubbing my cheeks to bring a little colour into them— for the summons had made me pale—and followed the woman. It seemed to me that I was walking a long distance through those rooms where the women all laughed in the manner that etiquette has laid down. A vague uneasiness filled my mind, and seemed to dull my senses and prevent my understanding what was passing around me. I was seized with a mad longing to fly, and felt that no earthly power could stop me, if I yielded to the wish, so lightly did my feet seem to touch the ground, and my thoughts flew far—far—to Doudou. I was stupefied to find that at that moment I thought of Doudou only as a refuge. Why Doudou, and not my Prince?—A mysterious instinct which in the moment of peril pushed me towards her who had nursed me in her arms when I arrived as a starving child at Stenia.

I saw from the manner of my conductress, that we were approaching the august presence of the Empress Mother, and instinctively I took the court pose, the upright body and the head thrown slightly backwards. Between two slim marble

F

columns I saw the Sultana sitting on a divan looking on the sea. I did not kneel down and place my face on the ground, for as I belonged to the palace, I had only to stand with my arms crossed on my breast. The Sultana was playing *tric-trac* with a young girl who struck me as marvellously beautiful. Her long fair hair was simply tied back with a knot of ribbon; on her neck sparkled five immense pear-shaped diamonds, and her white satin dress, cut square, showed a dazzling skin; on the bottom of her dress was a fringe of diamonds which produced a lovely effect.

Validé let her eyes rest on me, whilst I avoided meeting them—those wonderful, large, deep-set eyes, almost the colour of an emerald. A clear-cut oval face, with brilliant black hair cut short to her neck, which rose like a column. That is the picture that remains in my mind of the first lady of the Empire.

She asked me questions, but as etiquette

prescribes, I only answered to the third. Then she said gravely: " I wish that during your stay at the Imperial Palace you amuse yourself and be happy. I find you as pretty as has been said. You know how to amuse my son, our sovereign, and you are welcome. From now you will be our adopted child. You can sit down."

I sat down trembling on the edge of a chair, which was near me; and the game of *tric-trac* began again in silence; for the higher your rank, the less you speak, without something particular to say. By the silence of the beautiful fair girl, I understood that she was wife to the Sultan. She preserved a very humble demeanour to her mother-in-law.

I met the watchful glance of the young Empress, and I said to myself, " She knows that I am destined to be the wife of the Prince, and does not wish me to stand too high in the good graces of the

Sultan." As a point of fact no Mussulman thinks otherwise than fraternally of a woman whom he knows is destined for another. The respect and deference with which men treat women in the harem might well serve as an example to many men in civilized nations. The very few European men who have ever been admitted in harems always go away saying that " The women are treated as slaves." And why not ?—slaves serve their masters ; do not the housemaids and cooks in European households serve their masters ? So what seems strange to them here, seems natural enough at home ; but the lot of the Eastern slave is a happier one than that of the European servant. The slaves are like the children of the house, and the owner's interests are identical Supposing that there is no particular sentiment in it, surely it is to the interest of the master to look well after and care for the well-being of the person he has bought and paid for? I have never but once seen a slave beaten. Her case was a rare one. She had stolen two diamonds, and then they had surrounded her body with cushions to deaden the blows, and the eunuch who beat her took care only to strike on the padded parts.

When slavery is done away with, a grave error will have been committed, misery and prostitution will be doubled, and the slaves will suffer cruelly for their liberty.

When Validé Sultana again spoke to me, I had an instinctive desire to lay bare to her the conspiracy against her son. I grew pale and drew back when I felt myself on the point of making such a revelation; and I saw in imagination the bodies of the ministers hanging on Acq Merdan.

The Sultana made a sign to an attendant and said, "Conduct Ela Hanem to the chief treasurer, who will shew her my son's jewels," then turning to me and looking fixedly at me, she added gently, "There you will choose yourself a brooch from the first order, which you will wear as a remembrance of your stay here."

I entered the treasury with a smile on my lips, walking behind the guardian, but what I saw dumbfounded me—such a prodigious mass of precious objects, gold cups, arms, jewels, silks and furs.

"I should like to sit down," I said, and I heard that my own voice sounded dull and stupid—as indeed I felt at that extraordinary sight. I sat down on a sack of yellow silk, and from the feeling of its contents I thought it must be filled with amber beads, and I struggled to my feet.

"No, no, you can sit there," said the woman, "they are fine pearls and will not break."

"Allah!" I cried, almost afraid to look round, and though I cannot explain it, it made me suddenly feel sad.

But my companion understood, for she

looked kindly in my face, and said : "Yes, with me too it is the same when I see things so unusual. I never feel gay and never shall. For over fifteen years now I have been guardian of this mass of riches, and I feel stifled with it. It is too much, do you understand. Every Islamite brings what he finds here ; they would sooner sell cheaply to the faithful than dearly to the infidels. That is why for so many years precious stones, pearls, rare furs and magnificent stuffs have accumulated here, and will go on accumulating till the day comes when the Jews will seize them."

And then, as though both of us had some instinct of the future, we looked at each other solemnly.

The scent that there always is in rooms that are shut up and filled with stuffs, furs and boxes of sandal-wood made the air heavy and almost unbearable, and I said : "Let us go."

"Machallah," she answered, "but you

forget your brooch; follow me here." Then she and I passed through two more rooms like the first, and she opened with a key a third. Red and white cushions were ranged on stands, on which were pinned brooches, whose stones sparkled.

"Those of the first order are on the white cushions," she said in an expressionless voice, as if none of the jewels had any interest for her.

I saw a large ruby, the size of the palm of a little child's hand, surrounded with diamonds, with three large rubies like tears hanging from it, and this I chose.

"You are right," she said, "you understand." Then she took it off its cushion and gave it to me. I fastened it low down on my left side.

"No, not there," she said, with rather a sad smile. " It looks as if your heart were bleeding ; put it on the right side."

CHAPTER XVII

ONE afternoon I was alone in my apartment, when Taïfur Aga was announced. He entered looking depressed and pre occupied, and asked leave to smoke. Then he sat silently for some time.

I looked at him critically. I could not help admiring him; so well bred was his general look, and having a peculiar air of refinement and the saddest of eyes. He was always perfectly dressed; even his fez seemed better than anyone else's.

"Surely you have royal blood in you?" I asked.

"I know nothing," he said, carelessly, "I was stolen when I was quite small. But I have come, Ela Hanem, to confide a very grave affair to you. I have absolute confidence in you, for you are not like most women, and your ideas of honour are as pure as your beauty. I am obliged to confess to you—that I—I am not a eunuch."

In the East one must never show astonishment, so I did not even move an eyelash.

He continued, "I am about to become a father."

I could think of nothing to say except that I hoped the child would be a girl. Then, seeing that Taïfur Aga was much moved, I tried to quiet him by saying that it was said that such a thing had once happened in the Prince's palace.

"And what did the Prince do to the false eunuch?" he asked anxiously.

"He called him, telling him not to let it happen again. Later, when he died, he (the eunuch) left seven children."

Taïfur Aga then told me how he was madly in love with a young Circassian of the palace; how he had been in the habit of taking her flowers and fruit, and how she had fascinated him. She was always delicate and sad, but had welcomed him with so sweet and tender a smile that he had succumbed to her charm. He said he knew how much he was to blame, and how for a long time he had tried to stifle his affection for her by seeking amusement elsewhere; how he had kept a French *chanteuse* of the Pera theatre. Everything was useless, and he felt he must marry the girl, and he was determined that she must leave the palace; that he had come for my aid, adding: "And I know you will not refuse."

I could not refuse what the unhappy Taïfur Aga asked, and, having interviewed the doctor of the palace, explained to him in French that he must order the girl change of air as her health was suffering by living there.

Everything happened as we wished, without anyone having any suspicion. Taïfur installed her in Beicoss, a village in Asia, and doubtless became the best of fathers.

I mention this incident to shew how well guarded are secrets in a harem, and what might seem impossible in a European centre, with us becomes quite easy.

.   .   .   .   .

When I found myself with Taïfur Aga, who continued his service at the palace, I often led the conversation on the rights of the Prince to the throne of Egypt in the event of Ismaël's death. But he gave me no hope, and told me it was useless to hope that the Sultan would issue a fresh *irade* changing the order of succession to the throne of Egypt.

" In favouring the son of Ismaël to the advantage of your Prince," said Taïfur, " the Sultan is only preparing the ground for his own most cherished desire—namely, to change the order of succession to the throne of the Turkish Empire in favour of his eldest son, the Prince Imperial ; and

in a year's time the thing will be done.
I shall be very happy, because perhaps it
will give His Majesty the repose that he
lacks; though naturally," he added cour-
teously, "I regret that the interests of
His Royal Highness, your master, should
be in opposition to those of His Majesty,
for it could only be a happy nation if
reigned over by your Prince."

I did not argue further, and resigned
myself as a true Islamite to what was
bound to happen.

.   .   .   .   .   .

From the moment of my entry into the
harem of the Sultan I was perfectly free
to go out when I chose and to see my
Prince. Nevertheless, I feared since my
elevation to the title of adopted daughter
that it would necessitate a certain amount
of formalities.

Taïfur assured me that the honours due
to my rank would only weigh on me till I
reached the Prince's palace; and that from

there I could go and come, dressed as I chose, as a Turkish or European woman. "But," he added, "Her Majesty would be displeased if you absented yourself for more than two days, as she has taken a great affection for you, and puts more confidence in your devotion than in that of my older ladies of the court."

The kindness of the Sultan filled me with terror. I would have wished him to be hard, brutal, and savage, whereas, on the contrary, each day he seemed more kindly disposed towards me.

I asked Taïfur to give the necessary orders that I should be driven to the palace of the Prince the next day, and then I took from under the cushions of my divan a number of *La Vie Parisienne* which I had found. "You never read that," I said. "I am very curious to know who reads these things in the palace, and how they come here."

"Oh, it is very simple," he answered.

" The Lord High Admiral Prince M——— D———, who is now seven years old, asks for French pictures, and that is how it comes here ; but, thanks be to Heaven, no one who could read it would understand it."

Then Taïfur, who was smoking a last cigarette, got up to go. Suddenly we saw bits of furniture being thrown from the windows in the wing of the palace reserved to His Majesty, chairs and tables falling with a heavy splash into the sea.

" It is a new fit of temper," said Taïfur ; "all the furniture will have to go ; one can do nothing. Every time there is a presentation of credentials, our well-beloved master gets into a rage. He beats his ministers and throws the furniture out of the windows. He dislikes any European interference in his affairs. Since he was obliged to decorate an ambassador with the *grand cordon* of Osmanie, the finest cock in the Imperial yard struts about with the same ribbon round his neck. Nothing is more amusing than to see the bird walking proudly amongst the rest as if he knew of his elevation to a dignity that he shares with an ambassador."

"The ambassador is then French?" I said in fun.

"Yes," answered Taïfur, not understanding the malice in the allusion. "And now," he continued, kissing my hand, "since you are the best of Princesses, try and calm this Imperial storm."

When I entered the apartment of the Sultan, I saw a red satin armchair standing alone in the middle of the room. I immediately sat down in it, arranging my long train round me like a peacock. The Sultan, in his white *intari* with bare arms, walked towards me frowning, his eyes bloodshot, and his face transformed with anger. With sudden brutal strength he lifted the chair and myself and carried us to the window. There fortunately he stopped. "Machallah!" he cried, " for love of Mahomet get down, or I will throw you into the Bosphorus."

"Your Majesty surely forgets that I should be breaking all the rules of etiquette if I used your shoulders as steps. Will Your Majesty deign to put me down?"

The game was won, for he began to laugh, and placing me on my feet once more, he said, "You are the bravest of women. Ah! if my army——"

"Yours is the bravest, truest, and most devoted of armies. Pray God you will never have to complain of it."

"Well, why do you interrupt me when I speak? Ah! if my army were to take you as a model. I have a great mind to make a soldier of you—another Kara Fatma, would you like it?"

"Don't do it—there would be bloodshed."

"You say, there——"

"I say many stupid things," and then I could not help adding with a sigh, "but they are only to amuse you."

"Yes—to amuse me—to make me forget my bleeding wound. My life is one long torture, like Napoleon the First's or the Third's. Those are my brothers in tribulation. I have everything, and God has even given me more—and yet, day and night, I am haunted by the end of Napoleon the Third. All the ambassadors that are sent to me are only a threat to the Empire. When I see them bow before me, I see in each one the enemy that would stab me in the back—and I long to crush them all. Also," he added, lowering his voice, "I pretend to myself that all these pieces of furniture are the ambassadors. The first I threw out was the English one; the second the Russian; the third the Frenchman. The one you are sitting on is the Austrian,—the others are at the bottom of the water."

"Since I am sitting on Austria," I said with great seriousness, "she is no longer dangerous; let us leave her in peace."

Then we looked at each other and laughed, and he went on—

"I gave my minister of war a good beating—that idiot gets on one's nerves; he pursues me with his ambassadors. Those fools of ministers never will understand that it is from those quarters that all danger will come."

"Why does your Majesty think he will be attacked by a European power?"

"My child, I have no other danger but that one."

He dismissed me with those words, and I could not help wondering, as I went away, why it was always an imaginary danger that one saw, and never the real one that advanced with threatening strides.

Romance of a Harem   171

CHAPTER XVIII

THE ceremony with which it was
necessary to receive me, when I went
to see the Prince, struck me as absurd and
interminable. But I was anxious to see
him, around whom all my thoughts centred.
The jewels, pinned in profusion in my hair
or hung round my neck, seemed only a
heavy burden and a wearying chain. Slaves
threw themselves at my feet to kiss the
hem of my dress, which I gently pulled
away. My heart beat with impatience,
whilst my eyes wandered perpetually to the
part of the palace which was the Prince's.
At last, when the ceremony was finished,
I was able to send for my maid Louise, a
European, extremely pretty and good,
though devoured by ambition. For the

moment she was amusing herself with a flirtation with one of the secretaries of the Prince, whilst waiting for something better.

I quickly took off the heaviest of my jewels, and ran to the window, whence I could see the little steam-yacht of the Prince. It stopped at the landing-stage in front of the palace, and I saw him slowly walk up the steps of the quay and go towards the courtyard. My joy was so great on seeing him, that my very heart seemed to dilate and fill my whole body. I ran to meet him, and remained almost stupefied at the profound bow he made me. "Is he going to stay long in this position?" I said to myself, "bowing to the ground."

With that fever of love in his beautiful eyes that I loved so much, he suddenly came near to me (and looking hurriedly round him, with the uneasiness which those have who live continually in a crowd which spies on the smallest action), he pushed me gently into an inner room. I tried to smile, but overcome by the nearness of a happiness long dreamt of, I thought I was going to faint, for my eyelids closed and my head fell heavily on his shoulder. He put his face close to mine, and kissed me on the lips. We looked into each other's eyes with something of a sad mysterious wonder, holding each other closely. Then he stepped back, and I felt his hands tremble as they held mine.

"It is good," he said in a half whisper, "to know that one has the mastery over oneself, and it is a delight to me, loving you, as you know I love you, to hurt myself in keeping my word."

"Ah!" I said, "it only means that we do not know how to enjoy the hours God has given us to live; it is bruising the love in our hearts. That is what is called manly courage—the courage of a *grand seigneur*, who builds up an insurmountable obstacle, which honour bids him not destroy. Why —why obey a case of imaginary conscience?

Am I not sufficiently mistress of my actions to be able to judge concerning my own happiness, and to know what pleases me best? Why change our customs and make for ourselves a standard of European honour, when our own is sufficient for our happiness? Suppose I am of Christian race, I give it up to become of yours. My heart and soul is filled with distaste at the idea of any other life than that of a Turkish woman; and if I ever have the smallest reproach to make to you, it is perhaps that you have given me a European education. Why upset the peace and simplicity of our hearts with ideas that are not in keeping with our religion? How can you, clever as you are, believe in this system of education that destroys all sense of peace and happiness?"

The Prince began to laugh, and put his hand over my mouth. "Evidently," he said, "the results of progress in the harems are not very successful, and if it pleases

you, we will bring up our children otherwise.   But I forgot to tell you that the
Minister of War wishes to see you, and
you had better go to him this evening.
The great event is near, and it is a
serious moment in our lives.   When
everything is settled, then we will think
of our pleasures."

"Alas! our happiness will always be
thrust into the background for serious
business.   Ah! how I look back with
sadness on the old happy days when I
was a child!   How good you were to
me then!"

"And now?" he said tentatively.

I could not answer, for tears were too
near my heart and eyes.

.   .   .   .

That evening I presented myself at the
palace of the Minister for War, and he
put me briefly *au courant* with the
situation.

"Everything is ready," he concluded.

" I am going to Brousse ; my return will
be the signal for action. The day that
Taïfur Aga brings you a message from
my wife, you must be ready. I shall go
myself and bring Mourad Effendi to the
War Office, where all the ministers will
be waiting, and will proclaim him Sultan.
You understand perfectly, do you not?
You will wait for me at the door we
have decided on, and the moment you
see me you will go and tell Mourad to
come down quickly. At three in the
morning a *softa* will expect you on the
quay of Stamboul—the one where the
boatmen wait—and you must give him
this letter yourself. You must be dressed
en Cocona (Greek woman) so as to avoid
any suspicion. You understand?"

" Yes—yes, I know, I understand ; it is
all graven on my heart—all these things
that are contrary to all divine laws," I
said, and a sense of shame made me hang
my head and nearly overcame me, so that

I fell sobbing on the bed of the minister. I felt I was beneath the feet of destiny and powerless. A hand gently laid on my head brought me to myself, and I recognised the common voice of the wife of the Minister, who threw her arms round me, and said :

"Why are you crying? Pasha, what have you done to this poor child? Always these stories of revolution?"

She pronounced the word *revoludzione*, not even understanding the meaning of the word, though she knew vaguely that it was a menace to the Sultan. Very much upset, she hid her face in her hands, and began to cry, saying, "May curses rest on him who lays hands on the sovereign! May his hands rot off, and his entrails be devoured by the dogs in the streets!"

"Who says a word about touching His Majesty, woman?" said the Minister severely.

"Alas, that it should be so!" she sighed. She continued to cry for some time, stifling her sobs, for fear her husband should send her away. And he, wishing to change the current of her thoughts, promised to give her a yellow velvet dress, whereupon the large woman immediately dried her tears and proposed that we should finish the evening eating fruits, which we did, forgetting in that child-like pleasure the deeds of the morrow.

CHAPTER XIX

A LITTLE before three in the morning, sadly enough I went in a small hired boat towards the little ruined bridge of Stamboul. I was dressed like a Greek woman, and my heart beat fast as I landed, shivering from the chill damp of the sea. I looked anxiously in every direction—not a soul. I was alone in the great silence of the starry night. A dull fear seized me at not seeing a human being.

If the *coup d'état* is discovered, I thought, I am lost. It needs but that a single spy should have crept in amongst the conspirators. I looked into the dark waters of the Bosphorus, immovable and stained with the mud washed up by the current. I tried to guess at the depth and the possibility of escape by swimming. I thought at least I could, by plunging in, be able to go far enough without being perceived, and almost unconsciously I began to unfasten my petticoats, when I heard heavy footsteps at my side. I looked round breathlessly and ready to plunge in, when I saw a *softa* coming towards me, whilst five or six others stopped and deposited on the ground heavy potato sacks that they had carried on their shoulders.

"Have you the message, *cocona*?" the first *softa* said to me in a low voice.

I held out the letter to him, saying, "You are very late; in a few minutes the provision boats will be here to unload; we must hurry to get away."

He put the note in his sash and clapped his hands. The other *softas* came up, almost bent double by the weight of their burdens. They walked on to the little landing-stage and softly slid what they had carried into the water. Their various loads sank with scarce a sound.

"They are those amongst us," said the *softa* with a well-modulated voice, "that we suspected of treason." Then the mud and floating rubbish, that had separated for a moment, closed over again and made a heavy covering on the tranquil water.

. . . .

Presently the sun rose, with six clouds round it, like you see in the pictures of God in the English churches, and I found myself on the bridge of Galata as some Turkish soldiers were passing. One pinched my arm, another tried to put his arm round my waist, and a third kissed me violently on both cheeks. Two of the *softas* who were watching over me came up, and the soldiers hurried away, looking rather ashamed of themselves, whilst I said, so that they should hear, " It is better to sin and repent than not sin at all." The last of the three returned and offered me a rose he had in his hand.

CHAPTER XX

IT was to take place that very night. Standing still in my room, I remained motionless, expecting every moment to hear hurried footsteps or cries. I heard nothing but the thousand and one inarticulate noises of the palace—that immense gilded cage full of beautiful creatures, careless and happy.

Towards evening I put on as dark a dress as was permitted by the etiquette of the court, and putting together all the jewels I did not want to carry off, I placed them carefully in a silk bag, wearing only over my heart the great ruby.

"Ah, God!" I prayed almost aloud, "give me strength to accomplish my mission ; leave me a mind clear and strong, to save him or those who should be the victims of an order badly understood, or of forgetfulness in the terrible march of events this night—or of the unexpected which upsets all carefully arranged human plans." Some sort of instinct made me always afraid of the Sultana Validé, and at eleven o'clock I went towards her apartments.

"Listen, Ela Hanem," said the Empress Mother at once, "listen to the dull noise of the troops assembling round the palace. They are our brave soldiers, who from fear of some new manifestation of those impudent *softas*, are guarding my august son. Listen! —listen! it is a joy for the heart of a mother to know that her child is so well protected."

Some of those present wished to go and warn His Majesty of what was happening, but the Empress stopped them. "No," she said, "let him rest in peace, he sleeps."

. . . .

That night, as usual, by two o'clock there was absolute silence. The night-circuit made by the slaves would not happen again till three o'clock, and I made my way towards the room where the Sultan slept. Everything was quiet. No help could come from the court-yard, and the chief eunuch had the keys of the other entrances, so there was nothing to fear; but on the way to the door where the Minister of War was to await me, I met a slave who said to me in a trembling voice :

"I swear to you I saw a man with a beard enter the yard."

"Don't be stupid," I answered. "Go immediately to bed; I will go and warn the eunuch of the guard."

She at once obediently went to her room, and a short time afterwards I returned on tip-toe and saw that she was sleeping profoundly. Then, with absolute self-possession, I went calmly towards the spot we had settled on.

Opening gently a door, my hand met that of the minister. Without saying a word I

G

retraced my steps and stopped before a door ajar; I passed my hand inside, which was immediately seized by a young man, who came out and walked silently after me. It was Mourad Effendi. (The Sultan kept him in his palace so as to watch him the better). We went to the entrance door, where they awaited us. I opened it widely, and we saw before us, clearly in the wonderful moonlight, the Minister of War, in full uniform.

Mourad Effendi passed in front of me, and it seemed to me that he was trembling violently. I shut the door gently behind him and turning the key twice, hid it in a distant room.

My heart seemed to feel nothing, and it was with perfect calmness that I approached again the room where the Sultan slept. I lay down on the ground across the door and waited.

I heard so distinctly the regular breathing of His Majesty that I could not help

asking myself, whether it was the great silence that made the sound so clear, or whether it was the influence of the highly nervous state I was in, that made me conscious of what others could not hear. I was astonished at myself at being pre-occupied with such small things when so great a tragedy hung in the balance.

"How peacefully he sleeps!" I thought.

I heard the muffled step of the *Kalfa* on guard in the room next to his bed-room.

No one could enter the Sultan's room except by the door in front of which I lay, and the bed of the *Kalfa* on guard was the other side of it.

A number of slaves passed on their round, and I pretended to be asleep, and they did not disturb me. "Three o'clock," I thought; "in an hour the chief eunuch will be here."

The hour struck and then the half, and I felt that I must be like one dead to look at. That horrible waiting—waiting—seemed to wear out my heart, and I felt as if the last few drops of blood were dropping from it on the carpet—and I even passed my hand over the silk to see if it were real, so strong and agonizing was the sensation.

" May the hands of those who touch the sovereign rot off ! " I repeated almost unconsciously, and under my breath the words of the wife of the Minister of War.

Presently I heard a footstep, muffled like that of the niggers, and I saw coming towards me the chief of the eunuchs. I stood up to let him go past, when I saw he held in his hand the Imperial *irade*. He knocked sharply on the door.

" Open," he said, without a shade of respect in his voice.

The *Kalfa* on guard recognised his voice and opened the door. He went in, I following, and placing myself at the foot of the little iron bed on which slept the Sultan Abdul Aziz.

" Put on your furs and come down to

your boat, which will take you to the Vieux Serail," said the eunuch brutally.

"From whom comes this order?" said the deposed Sultan, with wonderful calmness.

"From the Sultan Mourad Khan."

The eunuch showed him the *irade* with the Imperial signature of Mourad, and again reiterated the order to immediately quit the palace. The Sultan said not a word, and slipping his furs over his night-clothes, took his arms, and walked out with a calm step. I took his hand as I followed him, and kissed it.

The courtyard was completely deserted—not a soul to be seen. The Emperor crossed it with his head up and an expressionless face. At the bottom of the stairs he met his eldest son and said to him:

"I appointed you Grand Marshal for our safety, and this is how you know how to protect your father." Then with a firm footstep he continued his way. Arrived at the white marble quay where his Imperial *caïq* was waiting for him, he descended the steps with that marvellous dignity which had always made the populace admire him so much.

He paused for an instant on the last step and looked with inscrutable eyes at the heavens, just blushing faintly under the rays of the rising sun. At the moment of stepping into the boat he let his eyes fall on those who were going to take him away The two officers and the twenty-four rowers immediately prostrated themselves, saying, "Pardon us, lord."

I wished also to step into the boat, but one of the officers cried out "*Yassak!*" ("It is forbidden!"), and I was obliged to retrace my steps. I crossed again the courtyard and the inner yard, with my heart torn at the sight of the palace, yesterday so full of life, now empty like an uninhabited country

On entering the harem I found a terrible *bouleversement* taking place. The women shrieking like wounded hyenas, were wrecking everything, and breaking windows, mirrors and furniture. A little fair woman crying silently in **a** corner, rose suddenly, opened a window, and threw herself into the Bosphorus with a great splash.

I went to my room through a mass of disordered and broken furniture; when I had lifted the *portière* and entered, I was surprised at the calm that reigned there. I took a shawl, with which I covered my head, and went out.

CHAPTER XXI

" IT is finished; but how did it all happen?" asked the Prince.

"Very simply; His Majesty made no resistance."

"And the harem?"

"Everything is being broken there."

. . . .

I had heard from my bed, where I had fallen broken and bent with fatigue and emotion, the hundred and one guns which announced the coming to the throne of Mourad. Then feeling that my eyes were closing, I called my slave and gave orders that no one was to be allowed to come in. A day and a night passed thus, and, tottering feebly like an invalid, I went to see the Prince. He took my hand saying, "My poor child, it is dreadful that you should be in such a state."

" It is over—it is over," was all I could say, turning away my face to hide my tears. Then I asked his permission to go to the Minister of War, telling him that I did not think we should let him forget us at that moment.

"I am of that opinion also, dear friend," he said, and I saw that at the sadness that I felt, and the despair he guessed was mine, he felt ill at ease.

The first sensation was, that things could never be as before.

On arriving at the Minister's, I found the harem full of the wives of the higher dignitaries of the State, seeking to gain the good graces of Hanem Effendi. There was a great coming and going of pashas, beys, and ambassadors, which shows that when things turn to your advantage, whether rightly or wrongly, the world will bow before you. Instead of feeling all the importance of my situation, and the necessity of keeping the position I had worked for, I longed to step quietly out of my door, leave my present life behind me, and never return.

It seemed to me that the great love for the Prince was dead in my heart, leaving me broken and unhappy. I waited for the Pasha a long time in the harem. At last he came in, holding his head very high, and with his eyes more brilliant than usual. He was in full uniform, and looked so imposing and full of authority that I shrank back instead of putting up my face to be kissed as usual. When in his room, he allowed his wife to undress him, who deluged him with questions.

"You tire me," he said to her, whilst I waited silently, judging that he felt as preoccupied as I did.

Suddenly he said, "Do you know, I thought I should be obliged to kill myself. I am going to tell you all about it as I rest a little. When you brought Mourad Effendi to me we went towards one of the gates leading out of the palace, and where I gave the pass-word, and the sentinel answered ' *Yassak* ' ('you cannot pass'), I said to Mourad. ' The soldier has made a mistake and has forgotten the pass-word let us go to another gate and make as little noise as possible.' Having reached the second and pronounced the pass-word, the same thing happened. I explained that I was Minister of War, and that I would have the sentinel shot it he did not let me pass. The brave soldier answered ; ' All this may well be true, but I have received my orders and I shall obey them ; you give a different pass-word to the one I have for the night ; you cannot pass, and if you are the Minister of War, I shall be shot—great is Allah!' Everywhere I received the same answer ' *Yassak*.' Mourad Effendi was nearly dead with terror, thinking that I had betrayed him, and he said to me in a voice I can never forget, ' What

have I done to you that you should lead me
into this trap? I never asked to be made
Sultan—it was all of you and Midhat who
wished it. It is then only a betrayal, that
you might make me die a terrible death.
The Sultan knows everything, does he not?
It has all been arranged beforehand—Allah!
—Allah!—my father, what have I done to
you? I am innocent!" In the bright moonlight I saw his handsome face distorted with
fear, and he cried like a child. I tried to
reassure him, but he no longer believed in
me, and I myself feared that there was
some treachery. I felt we were lost if we
could not find the means of escaping from
the palace. Seized with pity in the face of
Mourad's despair, I held out my revolver
to him, saying, 'If you do not believe in
me, kill me, and if you do not do it, I will
kill myself in your presence, if we cannot
save ourselves.' He was trembling in every
limb, but said distinctly, 'I believe in you,
my father, save me.' I took him by the

arm and led him towards the sea, along the interior quay of the palace. By God's grace at that moment a boat was passing. I hailed it, and placed the Prince in it, getting in beside him myself. In that terrible moment I noticed that the cushions were torn and shabby, and that made me look at the man who was saving our lives. He said his name was Hussein and that he came from Stenia. The ministers were waiting for us at the War Office, in the greatest anxiety. Mourad, having been acclaimed Sultan, signed the *irade*, which you saw presented to the deposed sovereign — and now you know the rest."

After a long silence, which followed this story, I said to the minister : "And when will the Sultan Mourad sign the *irade* giving back the throne of Egypt to my master ? "

"Very soon, my child; in less than a month it will be done. His Majesty also intends showering favours on you, and wishes to prove his gratitude to you. *Allons!* you will be the Vice-Queen of the most beautiful kingdom. Ah, my lamb, you will be a second Cleopatra!"

Without thinking much of what I was saying, I said: "I hope the health of the Sultan is good?" and then felt astonished at my question, and examined with exaggerated interest my nails, which from love of the ancient customs I had reddened with henna. The minister took a prolonged pinch of snuff, and passed his hand over his face. He explained to me that the Sultan wanted rest, that he had not got over the adventure, and his coming to the throne. "I do not know," he added, "how things will go off on Friday, the day of prayer, but I shall take him myself to the Mosque; but I fear they will see that he is on the verge of madness. It will be sad indeed, if he pays for his throne by losing his mind—he is so gentle and affectionate; but I fear he will not get over the shock; his terror was too great."

I could only answer: "Then he has become mad from fear, and it is you who will manage everything as his guardian, and it is you who will have to support the throne against all."

"With God's help, it is I, and no one will dare to meddle in what does not concern him. No one must guess that Sultan Mourad is afflicted with melancholia. I am going to live in the palace so as to keep guard over him; he throws himself into all the fountains in the harem, and thinks he is pursued by the Sultan Abdul Aziz."

"Have you thought how important it is that this misfortune should not be known? You know how much the populace both love and fear Abdul Aziz? Even on the day of his deposition, people only dared mention his name in a whisper; they were still afraid of his power."

"Be calm, my child; all will go well.

In a month at latest the *irade* that concerns
you and your Prince will be given. Do
not press for it before; I cannot do more.
Ah! by-the-bye, do you know what your
friend Nedjib Pasha answered to the
Sultana, who, when concealed by a curtain
asked him what reward he wanted for
having cut all the telegraph wires at the
moment of the *coup d'état*. 'Your Majesty,'
he said, 'give us a constitution, and not
diamond snuff-boxes.' 'My son,' she said,
'I am willing, but what is a constitution?'"

"And Midhat, what did he ask for?'

"Midhat—Midhat, oh! he likes being
talked of in the European papers, and here
he himself talks a good deal; but he is no
good—a man of straw—a coward." Here
the Minister took my hand, as if he were
working himself up to tell me something
disagreeable, and added: "I forgot to tell
you that the ex-Sultan excites himself and
tries to form a following for himself. I

have placed him and his harem in a part
of the Tcheragane Palace. He often asks to
see you. It would be a good thing to
remind him of the old proverb, 'Serious
diseases require serious remedies,' for if
he insists upon making trouble, we shall
be obliged to give him advice. I can, if
you are willing, give orders that you are
admitted.'

"It is well," I said ; "I will go to him."

CHAPTER XXII

HAVING returned to Prince Halim, I hid all my mind's anxiety from him, and repeated to him as closely as possible my conversation with the Minister.

"All that is naturally very tiresome for His Majesty, but we can count on the Minister's word," he said.

"Absolutely—ought I to go and see the Sultan?"

"Yes," he said, drawing me to him, and covering my eyes with his kisses. "I bore myself without you," he went on. "I live as retired a life as possible, and to amuse myself I paint all the portraits of my *kaftas*, and I try as much as possible to shew up all those who have powder on their faces. I think my harem should make the fortunes of the perfumers in Rue de la Paix. Perhaps my chief amusement is fishing."

" Yes, I know all that," I said, stepping back a little. " Your Highness is a great Prince, whose life can never be private "

The Prince lifted his cigar to his lips, and I looked at the enormous cabochon ruby that shone on his little finger at the same time feeling surprised that at such a moment my mind should observe so trivial a thing. Looking him critically in the face, I felt somehow that he was lost to me.

" I shall perhaps be his wife," I said to myself, " but never the woman he will love to the exclusion of all others ; it is over "

Without knowing it, I pressed my hand on my heart, where for the second time so agonizing a pain, that for a moment I felt dazed and stupid He looked at me whilst flicking off the end of his cigar

" What are you thinking of?" he said.

" I was thinking that you are rather like the Prince of Wales; your tailor dresses you in the same manner."

He began to laugh, and I added quickly, "Only you are better-looking."

" Thanks, dearest," he said, as he came towards me and pressed me to him. " Why do you worry yourself about my passing fancies?"

"God is my witness," I said gravely, "that I have confidence in the love of your Highness, and I only ask one thing, whilst I am away from you : that you do not love any other woman with the same tenderness you have given me. I know that you cannot remain faithful—for you are a great Prince, and all pretty and young women seek to please you; only let me please you more than the others."

CHAPTER XXIII

IN a vast room in the palace of Tcheragane, sitting on a dazzling white divan, the Sultan Abdul Aziz was looking sadly out on the sea. He did not seem to be able to take his eyes off a group of vessels that floated motionless on the sparkling blue water. They were the war-ships he loved so well, and in his fleet was the greatest sign of his power.

I entered the room softly and stood immovable by the door, even exaggerating my attitude of profound respect, ready to prostrate myself before the deposed king, wishing thus to show him that at least for me nothing had changed. Standing there I held my breath.

"Come near me, my child," he said in a

voice so sweet and sad that, forgetting etiquette, I ran to him. He gave me his hand to kiss; I kept it between mine, crying without a sob, though my heart was full of tears.

"You see where I am, Ela, my lamb—in the house I have built for the servants of my servants; but it will not be for long."

"Your Majesty will always be loved, whether you are in a palace or a hut. Everything will come right with patience, but I implore Your Majesty to be prudent."

On reaching the palace, which had become a prison for the deposed monarch, I had hoped to convince him of the uselessness and even danger of any resistance. I soon saw that I must give up all hopes of persuasion, and things showed themselves in their sombre and threatening reality.

An aide-de-camp, followed by two eunuchs, came to disarm him, in order to show him that he must renounce all idea of returning to power. Before his wonderful dignity the officer prostrated himself, humbly asking his pardon for the painful duty that was imposed upon him.

The attitude of the ex-Sultan was so dignified and simple in its grandeur that I lost what little joy there was left to me, and I suffered profoundly at the sight of the unhappy state in which Abdul Aziz now found himself; and I feared seriously that an attempt would be made on his life. I watched every night, not knowing how to protect him, feeling sure that if he persisted in trying to recruit followers he was lost.

I used to go to the Minister of War with peaceful words, trying to assure him of the better state of mind of the ex-Sultan. But the irritated expression on that officer's face often stopped the words on my lips. I grew more nervous about him daily; his supreme power made him less easily accessible than formerly, and I felt that he was becoming blindly autocratic. He invariably answered: "I have not the time now to attend to these details. Do the best you can; in a few days you will see the *irade* for your Prince; that is one thing done. You will see—you will see—I begin to understand more clearly what the future is for me."

I guessed what he meant by that, and felt frightened.

"Oh! go carefully," I said, with the tone of voice that one uses in the presence of death.

.   .   .   .

It was the hour of *siesta*. A great silence wrapped everything in the heaviness of the atmosphere. Abdul Aziz had a few minutes previously asked for a small penknife with scissors in it, that had belonged to his mother, and was trimming his nails. I felt weary and uneasy with a tremor at my heart, which is always an indication with me that something unfortunate is going to happen. Half dead with fatigue, I stretched myself on my bed, forcing myself to let my mind be a blank.

Suddenly I thought I heard hurrying and heavy footsteps in the room opposite. I ran to the window and looked towards the Sultan's room (the blind of his window was up). I saw a large jet of blood spring up towards the ceiling.

Instinctively I sprang on the window-ledge and was going to jump, when I heard his voice distinctly saying, "Do nothing, my child. *Yapma Kezem!*"

Recovering my presence of mind, I ran round as fast as I could, and crossed the room which separated mine from that of Abdul Aziz, and threw myself down beside him. Alas! I saw he was dying.

"They stifled me," he said with difficulty. "It was my former wrestler. I could not defend myself—or cry out—and my veins are opened.

I kissed him, as one would a saint, and then screamed as loudly as I could. The women ran to us uttering cries like animals that were being killed, and then fled. Validé Sultana entered slowly, and looking down on the dead body, she said in a deep, calm voice, but with such a depth of sorrow, hatred, and repressed passion in it, that my heart seemed to stop as I listened.

"Be sure, O lion that I gave birth to, that I will avenge you."

Then stooping, she took the celebrated ring off his finger. For a moment she stood motionless, beautiful and rigid, and repeated in her smooth, deadly voice, "You will be avenged; the dogs in the streets shall eat the pulsing bowels of those who have torn you away from my protecting love."

. . . .

I remember a general flight of the women, terror-stricken, and throwing themselves from windows, with piercing, half mad screams, and the beautiful body of Abdul

Aziz on an old carpet, which four soldiers carried to the guard-room of the palace. That is all that is left in my mind of that terrible thing.

Later on I learnt that, in the presence of the dead body, the European doctors announced that it was a case of suicide.

In the cemetery, in mysterious Stamboul, a single man followed the coffin of the unfortunate Sultan: it was the Minister for War. Not another soul — not a servant—not a slave!

CHAPTER XXIV

THE Prince, who was a man with real feeling, was much affected by the tragic death of Abdul Aziz. He tried to calm me, but I had been so much shaken by so many terrible events that nothing could bring a smile to my lips, and I remained dull and stupid.

Nevertheless, I did not want to lose all advantages from our previous efforts; and I worried myself at not seeing the issue of the *irade* which had been promised so many times. So I resolved to make one supreme effort. I had prepared the most beautiful of my boats and started towards Candili. I took a slave with me, and trunks, in which I had placed changes of clothes.

When Hanem Effendi, the wife of the

Minister, saw me arrive, she threw her arms round me saying, "Come quickly, my child; sit here and let us talk." And she began at once her conversation in her own language.

"*Kahbe Keze!*—I am sad, and you also, I can see it. You have got very thin; what will your lover say?—for men don't like thinness. But *yarabi*, if you knew how my heart cries! Do you see all the unhappiness that has entered this house, since we wished to live *à la franca?* It is my daughter that has pushed her father into all those terrible expenses. Formerly, when we lived in the old manner, we were always satisfied. Now the Pasha never is. What does he want? He is Sultan in deed if not in title, and believe me, my child, sometimes I think he means really to be so. Yes, indeed, *Allah Etmessine!* He has got that idea in his head, you will see. *Staafoulah!* I am wanting in respect to my husband in even thinking such things. But if I complain to you about the Pasha, my feeling to him is always the same. I honour him, but I regret that he has become so European. It is the fault of my child; may God forgive her! You see, Ela Hanem, children are doubtful pleasures."

She bewailed herself for some time like this, with the breathless, broken voice of a fat woman.

I stayed two days longer in the harem without being able to get a serious talk with the Minister. He seemed harassed and unsettled, slept badly, coming in just to have his bath, and going off again to preside over the night meetings. He looked very much aged when I saw him, and making me a sign to follow him, he said: "I had nothing to do with that sad affair. I had expressly given orders that he was to be surrounded with every care."

He was speaking of the murder of the Sultan Abdul Aziz. I nodded without saying anything. Hanem Effendi entered softly and sat down at the feet of her husband,

fondling them, and rubbing them with her hands. "To rest them," as she said.

"*Aman!* Pasha," she continued, "may God protect you!—but you know that Validé has sworn to avenge her son. Be prudent, and have yourself well guarded by the soldiers."

"Those are only women's ideas," he said lightly. "Soon I shall be so placed that nothing can touch me."

"*Allah! Etmessine!*" cried his wife, "what plan is in your head now? What infernal Christian book have you been reading? God curse those Christians, and may He burn them eternally in the hell that He reserves for them. We are indeed unfortunate——"

It was sad to see and hear the tears and plaints of that poor woman in their private room, where the Pasha, in full belief in himself, was thinking of the tremendous *coup d'état* that he was preparing, and which, without doubt, would certainly have

turned out successfully, if it had not been
for his tragic death.

I took his hands and kissed them, begging him to think well over it, and wait a
little; but I saw he was resolute and determined, and I could not but admire him
for that calm masterfulness which never
failed him.

"It is well," I said. "Only be a good
sovereign, and may God be with you!"

"He cannot be," his wife said solemnly,
and for a moment the common and rather
vulgar face of the woman became almost
beautiful with her determination to rest
faithful to her beliefs and sovereign. "God
can never be on the side of those who
perjure themselves; you are the head of
the army and you owe obedience and pro-
tection to your king."

"Machallah!" said he, smiling, "how
excited you are; do not let us talk any
more—I must be off. Have you any
commissions?"

" Yes—yes, I want some French candles."

" If I were you, I would be content with Turkish candles, and not drape myself with French stuffs," murmured the Pasha.

" Do not laugh at me, Pasha," she said gravely; "if we had stayed religious *à la turca*, we should be happier, not but what the giaours are not also honest; but what is good for them is not so for us, and what may make them happy can only render us miserable. Look at our daughter; if I did not watch her she would be too much *à la franca;* she would kiss the secretaries of the Embassy when meeting them."

At this threat of an embassy secretary upsetting the Mussulman ideas of Hanem Effendi, the Pasha, who was going out, turned and looked at me, and we could not help bursting out laughing.

CHAPTER XXV

EVERY evening, after an hour's peaceful and affectionate talk with me, the Prince got up, and, passing through the courtyard, went out. He got into his fishing-boat and went off to catch *lufer*. It is a pretty and exciting sport, and is done by the light of two flaming torches, one placed on either side of the boat.

Left alone, I followed with sad eyes the two lights which glided in the distance, and were reflected in the calm water like two large stars that had fallen from the skies; and I repeated to myself the words of the old Turkish woman: "To love a great personage is a thankless thing."

Secretly, I was devoured with uneasiness, and I searched in my mind for anything with which I could reproach him. I could find nothing that would stand any impartial analysis. He did everything to please me, forestalling every wish of my heart. I received from Paris all that I could desire in the shape of dresses, which were all laid out in rooms, where I spent many hours in examining them. Some secret instinct told me that I had lost that indescribable attraction which draws to you the man you love. It seemed to me that our love was no longer like a beautiful fruit covered with a delicate bloom, which no hand had ever disturbed, and I shivered when I thought of all that had passed, and what the inscrutable future might hold.

Where did he go every evening, like this? With my face buried in my hands laden with jewels, I could only sit and think of him. But my mind, shaken and tired out with recent events, was no longer clear.

One day I felt more miserable and tormented than usual, and getting up, I passed through the many rooms of the palace till I stopped before a *portière*. I lifted it and entered. Inside, a very old woman was sitting on a sofa, piously reading her Koran.

The old lady raised her eyes, and having marked the place where she was reading with a sweet-smelling marker, gave me her hand to kiss. Her hair, dyed red with *henna*, was bound with a red and blue veil; round this was wound a delicate white turban on which were painted butterflies, the whole making a startling note of colour.

I recounted to old Hanem Niné all the things that were disturbing my mind, and she answered me with the voice of a woman who was absolutely at peace with life and the world.

"You cannot hope, my child, to keep the noblest, best and richest of Princes entirely away from temptations. He loves *you* from his heart, but doubtless he loves others with the animal side of his nature. In a short time you will be his wife, when he will love you also from that point of view.

For the moment you must be resigned, since you wish to live the European life. You see, all unhappiness dates from that. You must be entirely Turkish or entirely European, but one or the other. For the last thirty years I have watched how much our customs have changed. Formerly a Mussulman would never have dreamt of a woman outside his harem. Now the exigencies of women brought up in the European manner have had this deplorable result. They will not hear of odalisques and several legitimate wives; consequently the Mussulman is obliged to imitate Europeans and visit women away from his household, so as to avoid scenes in his home. Consequently, they obtain great influence, because they become forbidden fruit. Ottoman families will soon become as disunited as those of the Christians, and of that state of things passionate crimes, hitherto unknown amongst us, will be born. Thus our Prince is in love with a slave, who is not of his service, and whom it is impossible to place amongst his odalisques. What can he do to have peace? He can but place her in a neighbouring village, where he goes to see her under the pretext of fishing."

"But," I asked, "who are the Mussulmen of to-day who have more than one wife?"

"There are no longer any, except the Sultan and our Prince; and as man is made to have several, he will take them from outside, which will be much worse for everyone. If you, the young Turkish women, will persist in your new ideas, you will make your husbands as bad as those of your Christian sisters, and then — *veselam!* it is finished."

"I agree with you," I said sadly, "but we have not yet come to having establishments in the towns, for a Turk sets too great a value on his repose for that. When he comes in tired from his business, he likes to put on his night garments and slippers, and tranquilly smoke his cigarette and drink his coffee. For the sake of peace in the harem he resigns himself to only one wife, but he is not less annoyed than resigned. Mahomet knew men only too well, and he knew also that God created polygamy, and that it were better so. I should be telling you a lie, Niné," I added, "if I said I were not jealous of this young woman whom our Prince goes to see every evening. But what hurts me most is that she has the charm for him of a woman who has been difficult to get."

In the gentle peace of Niné's room our voices sank into silence, and our eyes watched the twinkling lights on the Bosphorus. There was a tender melancholy that vaguely filled the evening air, but this restful charm was of short duration, for a voice called to me gently out of the dusk, " Ela Hanem, you are wanted at the harem of the Minister of War."

.   .   .   .

I got up quickly, and throwing a shawl round me I got into the boat that was waiting for me.

The Minister received me very affection-
ately. "I have sent for you, my child," he
said, "because to-morrow the *irade* that
your Prince is waiting for will be sent to
him in the usual manner, and I wished
you to be the first to give him the good
news."

I thanked him with effusion, kissing his
hand, as I used to when I was small. I felt
that my old affection was returning, and I still
admired him, though he, who formerly was
so simple, had become so ambitious. I felt
that the moment was swiftly marching on us
when he was going to try and create a new
dynasty—which would be his. I looked at
him curiously, with the conviction that he
would succeed.

"Hamid Effendi will never reign," I
began, when he cut my words short.

"My God, no!—he will never reign, and
that will be no misfortune. He is a Prince
who lives in daily and nightly terrors, which
prevent his having any judgment or ap-
preciation of things as they are. He has

only two serious qualities, order and economy."

" It seems to me," I said, "that for a pretender to the Ottoman throne, both those qualities have their value. I have often met him in the palace, and his serious and rather sad air attracts me. To his own people he is always gentle and sweet, and he is the least egotistical of men. He has even a great fault—for amongst princes he is too modest—he always tries to pass unnoticed. His fine eyes have no magnetism in them, and his look is that of a frank and honest man. He seems to give up all his mind to details. Every time I have seen him, he seemed plunged in thought—how best to manage his farms. Hamid Effendi is the best and most careful of bourgeois Turks, though he generally contrives to lose himself in the small details of life, but striving always to remain just and good. If he does not reign after his brother Mourad, he will easily content himself, for I have often heard him say, ' The Sultan is the most unhappy of all men, for he can never know the exact truth, and every one deceives him without scruple. Now that I know more about things, my life would be miserable if I became Sultan. I prefer to occupy myself with my farms than to spend my time unravelling the lies of the ministers!' And he has always said that with conviction."

"Leave him alone, he is a coward, he is even perhaps more so than his brother Mourad, who, from terror in a critical moment, has become mad. They are not men. Their father, Sultan Abdul Medjid, used to drink too much *raki*, and the children bear the stain of it. Those qualities of gentleness and goodness that you boast of in Hamid Effendi are very good, doubtless, in an ordinary person, but I consider them unfortunate in a sovereign. For the rest, do not let us talk about it. Effendi he is, and Effendi he will remain."

He took my face between his hands and kissed it, saying: "You ought to teach my daughter to sing like you do. You have a voice that stirs the heart; teach her also to play something of Wagner's."

"My God, Pasha, I don't understand Wagner, and I am sure she would not care for the noise of his music."

"Ela Hanem, I have seen the French ambassador, who told me that that music was the best. Personally, it gives me toothache, but I wish my child to be *au courant* in all that is the best and most fashionable."

His daughter—his daughter—how everything for him turned on those two words, "My child." To make a queen of her he had become a revolutionist.

Willing to please him, however, I went to look for Hairiee Hanem. I found her playing hide-and-seek with her husband, with little screams of delight. Seeing me, she made rather a discontented face. Without losing any time I sang her one of Wagner's most celebrated airs, when immediately Hairiee sat down at the piano and played it, with that wonderful ear for melody that young Turkish women have. Nevertheless, I began to feel a growing dislike to this young woman, who only used her father like a servant, and had the pretension and desire to pose as a Parisienne. I stayed some time longer at the house, sitting on a sofa and observing with consternation the change that had taken place in the harem, formerly so austere. Perhaps it is, that we have for so long kept to the ancient traditions that now we have gone to the other extreme. Quite suddenly everything was explained like a revelation, when with a whirl, there entered a young European woman with orange-coloured hair, and a dress that made one shut one's eyes.

"Who is that?" I asked in astonishment.

"Oh!" said Hairiee, "that is Mademoiselle Ines; for a long time she has bought for me all that I want." Turning to the newcomer she asked her what she had brought her.

"Some transparent cards, that you hold up to the light: they are very amusing—they have just come from Vienna." And this amiable young woman, with the aid of a candle held by a slave, proceeded to show the horrors of them. I saw that Hairiee had indeed become of the *dernier genre* from contact with the wretched creature.

I think that many Christian women are wonderful examples of virtue and honour, but these rarely visit us in our harems.

"Listen!" said Hanem Effendi in her coarse voice, "they are making a great noise in the courtyard. Ela, my child, go and see quickly what it is."

I picked up the train of my dress, and hastened to the courtyard. It was empty; the noise came from the big hall.

There, on the great table encrusted with jade a body was lying, which the servants in tears were crowding round. An aide-de-camp stooped and picked up long bloody ribbons, which he placed with care on the

table. Paralysed with horror, for a moment
I was uncertain whether what I saw was
real or not; then I hastened to the table.
The servants respectfully made way for me,
and I saw only too clearly. The dead body
of the Minister of War lay before me, his
bowels torn out, his breast laid open, his
eyes starting from his head, his mouth
open and full of flies. I drove them away
with my fan, and taking the poor dead hand,
kissed it. Almost without knowing what
I did, I picked up the remainder of the
entrails and pushed them into the terrible
gash in the stomach of the dead. I met
the eyes of the aide-de-camp, who must
evidently have thought that I was going
to faint, for he pushed a chair towards
me.

"Who did this?" I tried to say calmly,
knowing I should want all my presence of
mind in this terrible calamity.

"It was Hassan the Circassian, aide-de-
camp to the eldest son of Sultan Abdul
Aziz, and formerly aide-de-camp to the

minister whom he has just assassinated, some one answered.

"Thank you," I said, as if someone had done me a service, and I wiped my hands with my handkerchief.

.   .   .   .

The Minister and another were both killed in the council chamber. The assassin was evidently particularly ferocious and furious against our poor Pasha. They had struggled, and the Minister had defended himself bravely, trying to ward off the blows with a chair. Not one of the seventeen persons present having the simple courage to close with the murderer, except the old Minister of the Navy, who caught hold of Hassan by his tunic, trying to hold him back; but badly wounded in the face by blows with a knife (that the assassin gave him with one hand, whilst with the other he finished the murder of the Minister of War), the old man was obliged to let go. As to the other ministers of the council, with Midhat at their head, in a body they all took refuge in a neighbouring room, where they locked themselves in, waiting to be saved. Hassan threw himself against the door, shouting to those inside to open, saying that he would kill them all, and for such a sacred task Allah would give him supernatural strength.

" That, doubtless, is true," said Midhat heroically, through the door, feeling perfectly safe there, " but, my lamb, you seem to me at this moment angry, like a lion."

Below there were fifty servants in far too great a state of terror to come up to the help of the ministers.

CHAPTER XXVI

"DO you think that Hassan the Circassian did this in obedience to orders from the mother of the dead Sultan Abdul Aziz?"

"Certainly," said Taïfur Aga, to whom I recounted the event. "She has her vengeance on the death of her son, our well-loved sovereign, and she has known very cleverly how to take it. She knew that Hassan was passionately in love with the youngest of the dead Sultan's wives. He had seen the Sultana in her carriage, and since that, like the real impassioned Circassian, he had let himself nearly die of love, in thinking always of the beauty of the young Empress. Validé having learnt this, caused him to be brought secretly to the harem, and, hidden behind a curtain, she promised him the young Sultana as a wife, if he would kill the Minister of War and others. Hassan has killed him, as you know, but himself fell dead with twenty-eight bayonet wounds as he left the palace. Never mind, love made him brave. There is only one thing in this romance which distresses me : it is, that the Sultana he loved so much was his own sister, and he died without knowing it."

"How was this found out?" I asked.

"By a very small star which was tattooed under her left breast. Hassan was the eldest son of a Circassian chief. One day he had climbed into a chestnut tree to throw down chestnuts to his two little sisters who stood under the tree by the side of the road. Two horsemen came past at a gallop, hanging over their horses' sides ; each seized up a child, and before any one could come up at Hassan's cries, the two sisters were carried off—stolen and lost sight of for ever. When Hassan was fourteen years old, he started to try and find them. He thought that surely they must be slaves in some harem in Stamboul —not that he felt nervous about their fate; for he knew well that those kind of slaves have nothing to complain of. But he felt he would like to know where they were, and everywhere he gave that description that I have told you of—a little star tattooed under the left breast, and very distinctly done. It is a sign of recognition in his family."

A veil seemed to cover my eyes, something seemed to catch me by the throat, and my strength gave way. Suddenly I saw nothing, I felt nothing; a long way off I seemed to hear the eunuch's voice say, " Ela Hanem, Ela Hanem—*Varabi!* bring water— help—Ela Hanem is dying!" I had fainted. When I opened my eyes Taïfur Aga was looking at me, very much moved and rather frightened.

"I am so sorry," I said, "but my health has been so broken by all the terrible things that have happened, that the least emotion makes my heart stop. The truth is that on me also there is that little star, quite clearly, and I must be the other sister of Hassan the Circassian. I must go and see the Sultana, my sister."

I hastened to the harem of Abdul Aziz, where I found the young Sultana, who received me very well. It did not take us long to be convinced that we were of the same blood, and it gave us both the greatest pleasure.

She covered me with caresses and marks of love, and insisted upon my staying several days with her. We were only astonished that we had not found it out before, as our resemblance was very striking. And it could only have been in a place where two thousand five hundred people lived that such a likeness could pass unnoticed. Our story did not astonish the women much, but they

were all pleased with the romance of it.
Those sort of meetings between sisters are
not rare in harems, and they are the occasion
of many touching scenes.

When I returned to my master, I found
that his melancholy had very much increased.
The assassination of the Minister of War was
a fatal blow to his hopes, and he felt that
now his exile would last for ever, and each
day he grew more discouraged, for he saw
that Ismaël would remain master of Egypt,
and that he would never see again his
beautiful Nile flowing like a blue ribbon
through the fertile plain.

CHAPTER XXVII

A HUNDRED and one guns announced to the Ottoman people that Mourad Sultan's reign was over, that he was a hopeless lunatic, and that his brother Abdul Hamid had ascended the throne.

With him began a reign of suspicion and uncertainty. All those last terrible events, those intrigues and anarchy in the palace, given up to every one's fierce ambition, had only tended to make the character of Hamid Effendi more suspicious and uneasy; and in truth he became Sultan against his own wishes.

A few days after the assassination of the Minister of War, Hamid, whom everyone thought such a coward, having surprised two step-brothers of His Majesty Mourad in creating a scandal at the very door of the room (where the unhappy Sultan was struggling against his growing madness), drove them with a whip to the gates of the palace, saying, "To reign, without being able to rid oneself of such creatures, would lead one to madness or martyrdom."

As he was as Effendi, so he was as Sultan. His life was poisoned with the certainty that he could never learn the truth from any one. His first action on coming to the throne was to punish the ministers and generals who had betrayed the Sultan Abdul Aziz. One alone was spared, Nedjib Pasha, an amiable and honest man, who thought he was acting for the good of his country. His Majesty very well understood who it was who had induced the other Pashas to subscribe to the *coup d'état*, and he never felt any suspicion concerning the rectitude of mind of Nedjib Pasha.

The Prince apparently became resigned knowing that His Majesty was not too well disposed towards him. In the evening I used to read the papers aloud to him, but I soon saw that politics ceased to interest His Highness, and the reading only served to teach us how much the public is deceived if they believe what is in print.

One of Sultan Hamid's first cares was to re-organize his police intelligence department, which became one of the best in the world, which caused a European sovereign to say, "The Sultan is the best chief of police alive."

Thanks to two chamberlains who were very much *au courant* in the state of affairs, the Prince received as good information as His Majesty, and the way in which many things were mentioned in the papers, at least gave him a few minutes' amusement.

One evening he made his slaves bring two candelabras beside his sofa, where he was signing a few letters. Seeing him occupied, I went down to take a key to B—— *Kalfa*, the Chief Treasuress. Not finding her in her room, for a few moments I stood leaning against a window, and looking up, I could see the Prince quite clearly lit up by the two candelabras, his head and broad shoulders filling up the centre of the window that opened over the landing stage of the palace.   I leant out a little with my hands on my lips, meaning to kiss them to him, when I was horror-struck to see within a foot of me a man covering His Highness with a revolver.   In an instant, without a word, I dashed both hands in his face, tearing at his flesh and hair.   He pushed me violently away, and as he rar off and jumped into a boat, I saw the aiguillettes of an aide-de-camp sparkle in the dim light.[1]

I immediately told the Prince what I had seen and done.   He decided that we must keep the affair secret, and that he himself would tell His Majesty about it.

"Be prudent," I said to him; "your life is too precious that you should expose yourself needlessly."

---

[1] Validé Sultana, after this attempt, learnt that the Prince had done his best to save Sultan Abdul Aziz from death, and much regretted what took place.

" Precious ?" he said. " Do you think so ? My children are well provided for, and would easily console themselves in the event of my death. My life is absolutely useless. I shall never reign now, and all my plans for reform and the bettering of my country have become vain projects which I shall never carry out. There remains only to me the satisfaction of having dreamt of playing the part of an economical and just king, who would have raised Egypt to the rank of small and happy countries."

"Ah," I said, "my Prince, it is terrible to me that you should be so discouraged. Yours must always be the finest rôle in the empire. If you do not reign, you are at least the last of the Mussulman grand seigneurs. You have a tender heart, a great mind, and the most brilliant intelligence—so much so, that all strangers go away charmed with their visit, which they say they can never forget. You have the largest fortune in the empire. You are

the son of a king who founded a dynasty.
God has dowered you so well that all
sciences interest you, and you are adored
by your slaves, mamelukes, and even
European parasites who live on your
generosity. Those *chevaliers d'industrie*
and clever adventurers have made you a
little sceptical, but who would not change
places with you? Robbed always by them,
and deceived, why should you be eternally
duped? Your enemies reproach you with
avarice and parsimoniousness: are they not
those who have vainly tried to dupe
you? Hungarian generals, Polish princes,
French counts, Italian marquises, English-
men, and Bulgarian princesses have all
lived on you. They complain that they
can no longer get things out of you,
and that they are no longer authorised to
put on their cards, like the last Marquis
who lived at your Court—'Marquis de
T——, *Elephant Hunter to His Royal
Highness Prince ——*, Leave it to those
to defend you who know your generous

heart, unless indeed, they are ungrateful also. Though Maxime du Camp has said that 'Gratitude is not a rose that blooms twice,' there are still many hearts profoundly touched at the remembrance of your generosity."

All these brilliant and strong qualities the Prince certainly possessed. His one weak point was his suspicion of flirtations or love-affairs in the women he loved or had loved. At the smallest sign of anything equivocal, he condemned at once, and never pardoned. I ought to have foreseen what was going to happen to me, and living as I did a semi-European life, if I had an enemy who wished to ruin me, it could be done in such a way as to destroy the Prince's confidence in me. I lived entirely for him, thinking and dreaming of no one else, happy in the idea that in a few days I should become his wife, and in that happiness I forgot all past troubles.

.   .   .   .   .

One day, after drinking a glass of iced water, I felt very ill, and suffered horribly. The palace doctor was hurriedly called. He examined me, and, with an air of great mystery, succeeded in frightening me about my illness. The next day, however, feeling better, I wished to get up, but my European maid, with a hypocritical pained air, said, "Do not do anything so imprudent, Princess."

Nevertheless, feeling perfectly well, I began to read, waiting till the Prince should come to the harem.

The doctor paid me a visit, and lifting his hands to heaven, said, "It is death to you! What! standing up after that accident?"

"What accident?—what on earth are you talking of?" I replied in astonishment.

"Since it is a secret, I will speak lower," the doctor said obsequiously. "You ought to have confided in me, Princess."

"Indeed," I said, speaking louder. "what

is this mystery? Be good enough to forget that you are Greek, and speak the truth."

"Though I am Greek, I do not lie. You are on the point of becoming a mother."

"Wretch!" I cried, jumping up, scarlet with shame and anger at such a calumny. "You must indeed be of your race to thus dishonour a young Turkish girl. Cowardly brute, who has paid you to do this? What was the price? How long have you been spying on me? I have been well for so long a time that you found no means to carry out your vile conspiracy, and you were unable to ruin me. Leave the place—go! I see nothing but blood before me, and as there is a heaven above, I will kill you!"

Trembling with anger, I saw the round back of the doctor hastening away, preceded by an impassive eunuch.

This man had made for himself a very fine position as doctor in the Mussulman world. He was both respected and loved. It was forgotten that he was Greek, and consequently the secret enemy of Turks.

The Prince could not believe that a man whose reputation for honesty had been established so long a time could be guilty of falsehood. Nevertheless, he would not believe that I had erred, and he shut himself up, refusing to see any one, and taking his meals without leaving his room.

I suffered terribly when the *Kalfa* on duty refused to let me enter the Prince's rooms, and I experienced the agony of those long hours that those have suffered from who have been falsely accused without the means of exculpation.

I began to feel that death itself would be welcome.

In harems a passionate crisis like that is rare, and does not interest the world at large. Repose and rest are most valued, and exciting sentiments are considered only as European exaggeration, and rather tiring.

I was simply left to myself, not from want of feeling, but because they could not understand my despair, as they felt sure that I was guiltless—Ottoman women being very slow to believe evil.

At length one day I was summoned to His Highness.   Dressed in white—the only jewel I wore was the great Imperial ruby —I entered without nervousness, and held myself erect—as rigid as possible with my head up—and I looked the Prince straight in the eyes.   But I saw he looked suspiciously at the jewel I wore and at my figure.   Then I knew that for ever I was ruined in his heart by the doubt that I saw in his eyes.   He was lost to me, and my life could be but one long martyrdom. My heart beat and throbbed in my breast, like the flight of some poor animal mortally wounded.

"Do you think me a girl capable of lies and creating scandal?" I said, looking him straight in the face.

He turned his head away, and I saw his

eyes wander out over the distant country. For 'one instant he seemed to hesitate. I stooped down and kissed his hand with deference, and walked slowly to the door; I passed out—and I never saw him again.

The next day I wrote to him as follows :—

"Your Highness, having lost your love, my existence near you becomes a suffering for me that you will understand. I know too well the generous feeling with which you treat those who have served you faithfully, to hesitate a moment to ask you in which country or place ought I to live in exile or forgetfulness."

. . . .

The first lady of the harem came to me two days later and told me that I might, if I pleased, settle myself at Imirghian, not far from the palace, in a pretty little house by the side of the Bosphorus. I lived there for many long months amidst my devoted slaves. With the same sad feeling, I watched without growing weary the boats that passed beneath my windows. I looked in my glass to try and find my former beauty, but I saw but a faint remembrance of it.

I

Without strength or volition I spent long hours on my sofa. When a boat with three pairs of oars flew over the water, with the whistling sound of a bird, I knew by the agonizing beating of my heart that it was the Prince who passed; and hiding my face in my thin hands I stifled the cries that I longed to give, for my heart was bleeding—breaking. I was not dangerously ill, for it was worse than that, and by degrees I lost for ever my natural vitality. When my mind recovered from the shock, and I could look calmly in the face the position that fate had placed me in, I opened the Koran and read it every day, moving my head to the rhythm of the soothing and consoling words of our Prophet. I prayed every day, and understood that in simplicity of heart alone could one find happiness.

CHAPTER XXVIII

THUS I lived for two years in disgrace, without complaining, when one day I had the pleasant surprise of a visit from Taïfur Aga. He was much changed to look at, and with tears in his big eyes told me how unhappy and depressed was the life in the Vieux Sérail, where all the wives of the dead Sultan Abdul Aziz lived, deprived of all the comfort and luxury they had been accustomed to. They had become the prey of interminable boredom, their only amusement being walking in the mysterious and sad garden, where daily the cypress trees seemed to grow blacker and more funereal.

" They know," he said, " neither life nor the value of money, and what is left to them they spend in a senseless way. Their eyes are so full of sadness, that I go as little as possible to the harem, so as not to see it. Consumption has grown amongst them and makes wonderful strides, though the doctor says it is not infectious."

Then with a vague hesitation he took my hands in his, and said : "You ought to go and see those poor princesses. Ah! Ela Hanem, do not refuse. Validé Sultana hopes that you will be able to tell her of some honest person who will go and sell her jewels in Paris, where a better price could be obtained for them than here. We have not big enough fortunes here in Turkey to buy such stones, and the Sultana will not have anything to do with the Jews."

In silence for a few minutes I watched the soft plunging of a porpoise in the waters of the Bosphorus. I could not answer, for in my leaden heart I felt a renewal of my sufferings in the sad past.

"Will you not obey the orders of Validé because she is ruined?" he asked sadly.

So deep was my pity for her—so deep the pity for myself—that I could hardly trust myself to speak, but I told him I would go, and that immediately.

Three slaves brought me my *yashmak* and my cloak, folded away in a satin bag, whilst another held a silver glass before me. Somehow it gave me pleasure in carefully arranging the *yashmak* and slipping on the cloak of mauve silk. Then I turned to Taïfur Aga, and said, " I am ready."

" You are still pretty," he said, seeing me veiled in the *yashmak*, which beautifies every woman.

" That is of no importance now," I said gently, " for I no longer care. Let us start."

Of my former state I had kept nothing but a *caïq* with six oars, for I liked the way it was ornamented. The *hirame*—*i.e.* the carpet, which is placed at the back of the boat and trails in the water—was of green velvet studded with silver fish. At the two ends of the carpet, fastened by slender gold chains, were ten other big silver fish, which, when the *caïq* passed quickly through the water, swam behind it, and sparkled like diamonds. The cushions and dress of the rowers were also of green velvet embroidered in silver.

Sitting at the bottom of the boat were two slaves in rose-coloured satin, whilst Taïfur Aga held a large umbrella over me with a fringe of small pearls.

I looked with affection at my faithful Hussein, my chief boatman, who immediately dropped his eyes in token of respect.

"To the Vieux Sérail on the European side," ordered Taïfur, and the third boatman with his boat-hook pushed us swiftly out on the water. That good Hussein, from Stenia, had never left me since the day I first jumped from his boat and swam towards my destiny. It was he who arranged everything for me outside the house. He bought the provisions, and did all commissions; and often the little money that he earned he spent in trying to procure something that would distract my sad thoughts—his ideas being as touching and pathetic as they were simple. And then I used to gently scold him, saying, "Hussein, my little father, you are poor, and yet you deprive yourself for me!"

"Please God, Hanem Effendi, my lamb, my child sent by Allah, dear mistress powerful and noble, we shall become rich again."

For Hussein all troubles faded away when he had before him a cluster of raisins, some nuts and strawberries. His simple soul was a perfect type of the land of Islam, which seems so simple and perhaps ignorant in the eyes of Christians, but which has the good sense to be contented with what Allah sends and does not look for the impossible.

. . . .

When I reached the presence of Validé, I remained standing in an attitude of submission. The fallen queen did not speak to me until a quarter of an hour had passed, and I remember that I trembled with emotion.

"I have summoned you," she said, "to tell you to find someone trustworthy, who will take three of my tiaras to Paris to sell, and also to tell you that, knowing that you helped the Minister of War to effect the escape of Mourad Effendi from the harem of the palace, I have punished you for your fault. Your life has been spared, but the love of the man you cared for has been killed."

(I learnt afterwards that the Greek doctor had promised Validé Sultana to cause me to fall into disgrace, without explaining to her the means he would use to accomplish it).

"When the Minister of War," she continued, "found himself that night face to face with sentinels who had not the same pass-word as he used, there was no treachery on the part of the Pasha General. It was the Minister himself, in his anxiety, who forgot one word of what had been settled as pass-word. He was so afraid that his *coup a'état* might miscarry that his memory failed him, and he substituted a very similar word to the word chosen. God saved you all by the accidental passing of a poor boatman with his boat, when the Minister and Mourad were on the quay. For the chief eunuch was watching in the courtyard and had the keys. And you who went hand in hand with traitors—what have you to answer? Mourad is mad—and the other, over there in the cemetery, what does he do? Look for his entrails? half of which were eaten by the dogs in the streets. Your brother, Hussein the Circassian, kept his word: he tore out the heart of Hussein Avni Pasha, that cursed traitor! His eyes were torn out once, but I wish that they could see again, so that a hundred times they might be dragged from his head. Is that well?—answer."

Now I trembled no longer, and I

answered the fallen Sultana firmly, " Hussein
Avni was a great patriot.   He thought to do
well, but he sinned, for God has punished
him so cruelly.   But I—I am not ashamed
of being punished, for I deserved it, and it
is just."

"Nevertheless you loved my son, our
king?"

"I did my best, I could not do otherwise."

"You have sinned much, but you largely
repaired your fault by your devotion to my
august son when fallen.   He lived—is dead
—and has disappeared.   May God forgive
you, as I do."

A rush of tears came from my heart to
my eyes, and I fell at the feet of the
empress, hiding my face in the folds of
her dress.   I wept bitterly—passionately,
whilst she also cried with the tears of a
mother, holding each other tenderly.   Both
of us Circassians, stolen in childhood from
little unknown villages, so far away.   Both
of us beginning as slaves, then widely

different in position, and now, in each other's arms, through misery and grief become alike again.

Presently she said to me, "My child, my son loved you as a woman that one desires. But he never told you so, because being loved and destined for another he held you sacred If your life has been spared, it is to his love that you owe it. I wished only to punish you in the life of your heart."

CHAPTER XXIX

I SETTLED with Sultana Validé that it were better for selling her jewels that I should go and see Madame X——, lady-in-waiting to the Egyptian Princess Az——. This lady was starting the next day for Paris, where she was going to sell the jewels of the debt-laden Princess. She had in Paris, an intimate friend—a business man, R——, who was going to help her in this delicate business.

Princess Az—— assured me that I could place entire confidence in Madame X——, to whom she had confided the best of her jewels.

I hesitated for a long time to trust the three tiaras of the fallen empress to a European; and then, instead of doing so,

I gave her my brooch of large Imperial rubies, and said to her, " You know, Madame, that these rubies are of immense value. I beg you to sell them, and send me the money as soon as possible, making the necessary deduction for the commission." Quite happy with the idea that this money would enable me to persuade the Sultana to wait, I gave her back her three crowns, telling her that as the Sultan had agreed to augment her pension, it was better to keep the jewels.

" I swear to you that you will have the money soon," I said, meeting her rather incredulous look. I told her a white lie, for I added, " I have just met N—— Hanem Effendi, whose husband is constantly with the Sultan. It is she who has given me such good news."

. . . . . .

Madame X—— never came back. She stole the diamonds of the Princess and also my rubies.

Monsieur R——, who had a house in the

Bois de Bologne, was not content with only helping Madame X—— to steal jewels from poor Turkish women, but for other deeds, a few years afterwards, was obliged to fly. His fine house was in the hands of his creditors, and the whole business interested Paris for a few days. They have done everything they can to forget it, but doubtless in one or two harems it is still remembered where in that business they lost their last resources.

When I told the whole thing to Validé Sultana she summed up the situation by saying, "One ends by having to go to the Jews."

Then the conversation turned on European civilization. Validé gave it as her opinion that each country should be left to its own customs, and that real civilization would be to be tolerant.

"I do not know," she said, "whether Christians or Islamites are in the right. Allah alone knows. But we are the most discreet, and we never send any religious man amongst them with the idea of teaching them our religion. Why will the Europeans always think themselves in the right? They consider us as savages in darkness. On our side, we think the same of them, but our religion does not permit us to say so. Do you remember those two wives of the diplomats who came for the Treaty of San Stefano after the Russo-Turkish war in 1877? Both of them were received by the harem of the Grand Vizier. They did nothing but criticise our morals. The English-woman, Marchioness of X——, speaking to the wife of one of the pashas who served as interpretess, asked her to say to the wife of the Grand Vizier, how sad it must be to live in Turkey where there was no real nobility. The wife of the Vizier politely answered that the Marchioness was right in saying there were no hereditary titles, but nobility of heart was the more often found, and that, from a Mussulman point of view, was the most valuable. That great English lady continued to wound the feelings of the harem of His Highness by expressing a desire to see the daughter of the Vizier dance a Turkish dance. Hanem Effendi blushed painfully, and, losing her patience, said that if the daughter of the English-woman would dance an English dance first, the daughter of the Vizier would follow with an Oriental one. As to Madame Z—— the wife of the French diplomat, she reproached the ladies with not being charitable. " Your excellency is in error," answered Hanem Effendi ; "the Mussulmen share voluntarily with the poor, and if all the great personages did the same, there would be no republic in France. Charity and hospitality are two qualities we pride ourselves on. Be good enough not to judge us severely. We also in our country are *grandes dames*, and we do not forget that we have the honour and pleasure of receiving you."

Validé let her rosary of amber and gold beads slip through her fingers, and after a little silence she continued with her sweet, grave voice : " Europeans treat us as women of no importance ; but what would they say if they received us, and we behaved in the same way ? From a Mussulman point of view they are not well brought up, and from a European standpoint, we also are not. Which proves that what is good in one country is bad in another ; and the wisest is to do your best according to the customs of your own country, without trying to make others see things as you do. Those Christian missionaries are men of bad taste, and if they were not so ignorant, they would read the Koran and stay at home."

. . . . . .

On leaving the Sultana I was stopped by the chief lady of the court, who came up to me and said in a whisper : " If you have any money, order some bread to be bought to feed the ostriches in the garden ; the poor things are starving."

Instinctively I looked at the magnificent

ruby and diamond necklace that sparkled round her throat.

"What is the use of looking at that?" she said sadly, guessing my thoughts. "You know, my friend, we cannot let ourselves be robbed."

"Allah," I murmured, "take courage, my sister. The glorious Ottoman Empire will rear itself up again."

Then hand in hand in silence we walked through the gates into the immense garden. Everything there was falling to pieces. Marble columns lay in the long grass. A little further on, on a mound a kiosk was gradually disappearing. Already the tiles and ornamentations of the last century were falling from the walls, and making on the turf a miniature cemetery. One corner of the roof had completely fallen in, and on the top of the wall, which remained for the moment intact, a stork had built its nest. Through the old trees of a dead sad green, we looked towards

the Asiatic coast of the Bosphorus, where
one could distinguish a few white minarets.
Softly we heard a voice summoning the
Islamites to prayer. It was that of the
muezzin on the European side, who sang
with a broken voice, as if tired of living.
In the complete silence of that deserted,
overgrown, and sad garden the voice
reached us, wandering like a spirit through
the dark green paths—vague, sad, mysterious, but falling on the human heart
with almost a feeling of calm restfulness.

CHAPTER XXX

SOME years after the events I have described, I was asked in marriage by A—— Pasha, first aide-de-camp of His Majesty Abdul Hamid. I refused the honour, but it did not prevent my remaining on friendly terms with the direct surroundings of the court. The delicate health of Abdul Hamid never improved, and he suffered terribly from neuralgia. But always forgetful of himself, he continued to work and interest himself in all things.

One of his young aides-de-camp, a Frenchman, son of his old tutor, was drowned in the Black Sea whilst yachting, and His Majesty reproached himself bitterly and unnecessarily for not having had him better looked after. " It was my fault," he said, and for a long time grieved much over it. He has been always abused for having, as was said, been in favour of the war with Russia; but the truth is, when war was declared he was in despair, and the *kalfa* who watched at his bedroom door used to hear him crying and saying, "*Biti-Biti*" ("It is finished"). He ordered all the women of his harem to make cloaks for the soldiers.

Amongst other things they accused him of was, of following in all things the advice of his coffee-bearer. Why that man had so much influence with him was, that he alone told the Sultan the truth about things, and hid nothing from him. Again, it was said that the Sultan was not generous; but Princess B———, a European very well known in Paris, who was waiting one day to play before His Majesty, can affirm to the contrary. For three pieces that she performed, he had sent to her a tiara and necklace of great beauty. They reproached him for dressing the ladies of his palace in Indian muslins and woollen stuffs made in Turkey, instead of covering them with gold and pearls, though it is true that the ladies would have preferred these latter. His first care was to control the finances of the Empire, and putting things in order in his own household. For some time he tried to re-establish the industry of weaving those pretty stuffs that were made at Brousse, by making known to the ladies of the harems of Constantinople that he wished to see them as patriots, and dressed only in clothes made in Turkey. They pretended to yield to his wishes, but the eternal Mademoiselle got the upper hand, and persuaded the ladies to have their things made in Paris.

If His Majesty was influenced by morbid fears, as has been said, he is only to be pitied, for alas! his suspicions were only too well justified.

They say that the young party in Turkey

are dreaming of dethroning Abdul Hamid. They know nothing, or next to nothing, of the mind of the heir presumptive, the brother of the Sultan, and possibly are only throwing themselves in further complications. Let them at least hope that he may be an authoritative sovereign, energetic, and with a strong will. The expression in his eyes, if I were the youth of Turkey, would make me think—and perhaps doubt. *Allah Kerim!*